And the River Run

Cold Case Murder Mystery of

Leah Marcus

A True Crime Novel

By A. J. Ullman

Also By A. J. Ullman

One In A Million

Hit Or Miss

*Drifting, Falling — Diary Of A Call Girl
Suicide*

Praise for *And The River Runs Deep:*
The Cold Case Murder Mystery of
Leah Marcus

A. J. Ullman gives us a fascinating account of a fictional murder and murder trial that is all too real. It is set in Cincinnati, at a time of ... a race riot. As a lawyer and one-time Cincinnati resident, I liked all of that authenticity. The author's training in law and medicine shines through in his presentation of the forensics and procedurals, which readers of true crime will appreciate. I have taught legal ethics for almost forty years, so I also liked the way that the author wove into his narrative the ethical problems facing criminal defense lawyers. Having dissected many old criminal cases, I also appreciate the fact that looking back at outcomes, one is almost always left with a sense of uncertainty and unease, and Ullman serves it up with a jolting twist. The story is fast-paced and loaded with detail about the workings of the criminal justice system.

—Richard H. Underwood, Professor of Law at the University of Kentucky College of Law, and author of *CRIMESONG: True Crime Stories Behind Southern Murder Ballads* (2016) and

GASLIGHT LAWYERS: Criminal Trials and Exploits in Gilded Age New York (2017).

This novel was one of the most intriguing and exciting murder mystery novels I have ever enjoyed. A true must read for any Cincinnati native or visitor that loves solving mysteries. It took me on a fascinating historic journey of Cincinnati, Ohio during the infamous "race riots". An extremely talented and bright young women just about to let her star power shine bright was extinguished in a horrifyingly brutal fashion much too early... You can decide if the right person was convicted. You will be shocked and amazed at the human psyche when you finally find out who murdered Leah Marcus.

—Dean Visk, MSN, Director of Clinical Services at a national health insurance company

Praise for *Drifting Falling — Diary Of A Call Girl Suicide*

A. J. Ullman's writing is as sexy and smart as his characters in this dark but enlightening cat-and-mouse game about a troubled call girl and her beguiled therapist.

—Jim Debrosse, author of *Hidden City*

In a voice at turns wry and tender, Ullman brings to life a woman who may be damaged by the dark roads life has taken her down, but it's her strength readers will remember, her singular sense of self. Not since *Alien* has a Ripley been more riveting.

—Deborah E. Kennedy, author of *Tornado Weather*, an Oprah Top Ten Read for the summer of 2017

Once you start it, you won't be able to put it down and whatever you do, do not skip to the last chapter.

—Ross M. Evans, Esq., former Prosecutor, Magistrate and now in private practice

Cover art by Dave Flege and Shelley Savoy

This book is a work of fiction.

To my personal muse, Marjorie, for whom true
life feels like the best of romantic fiction.

And the river runs deep

And the water's cold as ice

-- J. J. Cale

Prologue

I never knew Leah Marcus. She was a girl, on the verge of young womanhood, brutally murdered in her own bedroom in an upscale enclave of a mixed-race neighborhood in the city of Cincinnati. The same city that Mark Twain once opined that he hoped to be an inhabitant of when the world came to an end, because then, as now, as everyone knows, Cincinnati is twenty years behind the times. That aphorism, though, appears somewhat suspect given some of the racially charged atmospherics of Leah's case that played out all over the country just a few years later.

Her life's story has become my own work. It was improbable that we ever would have known each other; at the time of her death, I was twice her age. We were not contemporaries, and the likelihood of our being colleagues or neighbors would have been slim. She was a rich girl from an affluent family who lived on the east side of Cincinnati, Ohio. I was a woman of Appalachian descent from the west side of town, a gulf wider than the seemingly boundless chasm of the Mill Creek Valley spanned by the Western Hills Viaduct that crossed over the visible barrier, Interstate 75, that split the city in two.

But our lives were bound together, hers at least by virtue of her murder, mine by being the then crime reporter for the *Cincinnati Tribune*, one of the daily newspapers of the city, at a time when daily newspapers were cherished institutions and being the crime reporter for the paper of a mid-size city was a big deal. The world of journalism now looks nothing like the bright future I predicted. Then, I was a recent graduate of Ohio University, where I, the first hillbilly ever from my family among generations of such children ever to have gone to college, majored in the journalistic arts. My professional education did not begin right out of high school. I had several detours along the way, waitressing at different restaurants, working a bookstore downtown, and giving birth at age twenty to a wonderful daughter. I soon realized that her father and I would never be compatible, and severing that relationship, knowing that I had full responsibility for the care of this child, decided to go to college, a single mom.

College, despite being at a school renowned for its party habits, was not a drunken splurge of sorority parties. I had a mission, a scholarship, an apartment in town, daycare for my girl, and a regimen of study that earned me a 4.0 GPA and a slot on the student newspaper, the *Post*. I graduated with a degree in journalism, *summa cum laude,* and with membership in Phi Beta Kappa.

After graduation, I scored a job as a cub reporter for the *Cincinnati Tribune* and, over a few short years, worked my way up to crime reporter. My job was to follow criminal cases that were newsworthy—typically murders, from the time of death of the victim to the arrest of a suspect, through the court proceedings and trial, to, if necessary, the scene of the death chamber at Lucasville State Prison.

Never as a journalist did I dream that I would write true crime, that tried and true genre that captivates the public and has spilled over onto television. There is a certain schadenfreude effect at reading about or watching other people's miseries with a breathy comment along the lines of, "There but for the Grace of God..."

Real murders are solved, if they are ever solved, within the first forty-eight hours after commission of the crime. This well-worn crime statistic is part of the bible of criminal investigators, because as the trail goes cold, the chance of catching the perpetrator diminishes. Few people confess to murder forty years later as they breathe their last. Those deeds they take straight to Hades, veiled in mystery as their own stone-cold corpse lays under a diaphanous shroud on a deathbed.

Most murders are committed by people who knew the victim; the police are well aware of this statistic, too. Most murders are not perpetrated by sophisticated, handsome serial killers like Ted Bundy. The typical killer is male, not particularly bright, and slips up when talking to the detectives and before the lawyer arrives, or as part and parcel of cutting a deal to avoid lethal injection. Few crimes are actually solved by journalists years after the fact. Despite the odds of such an outcome, I consider it my sacred duty to find the truth of Leah's murder.

Leah Marcus's death held the city spellbound during the spring and summer of 2001. Her murder—the alleged murder of a beautiful, young white woman at the hands of a black man—gripped the city like so many crimes involving sex, race, and class. This was a time forever etched in my mind, wrongly, as it turned out, as one of national innocence, before the horrors of 9/11 made it clear to the whole world, and most noticeably to us as privileged citizens of the USA, that the American century was fully and finally over. In those months prior to the national tragedy, a smaller Greek, or perhaps Shakespearian, tragedy was playing out on an unlikely stage, the midwestern city of Cincinnati.

Our country, and my former city, have a mixed record on race relations. This is the result of the by no means unique American institution of slavery, which, to this day, colors matters of civic discourse between members of ostensibly one cohesive society but, in reality, a fractured set of cultures and subcultures.

Cincinnati police officers had on numerous occasions shot and killed unarmed black men, and the city was, by the spring, seething with a lid covering the cauldron. But the steam leaked out. It would all come to a cataclysmic head in early April when the cover finally blew off. Amidst that explosion, one particularly nasty crime, unrelated to the riots, but perhaps not, would captivate the city for months.

Numerous innocent white victims were assaulted by the mob in Cincinnati. Leah Marcus wasn't directly one of those victims. But indirectly, she was as surely a casualty as if she had been standing at Ground Zero when the towers came tumbling down a few months later.

Chapter One

North Avondale

Her mother found the body. On the floor of her daughter's bedroom, naked, hands tied behind her back, lying on her left side, with a cord wrapped around her neck. Leah Marcus died at the age of seventeen years and eleven months, the victim of a murder and possibly a sexual assault. She was, by all accounts, a fine young woman. "Someone who was going places," said Vernon Banks,[1] the creepy neighbor who lived three doors down the street and who was the first person other than Leah's mother and the police to hear the news, courtesy of the police scanner he often listened to. Mr. Banks himself, briefly, would be considered a suspect. She was a National Merit Scholarship winner, as well as an accomplished musician, and heading off to Harvard University, her father's alma mater, in the fall after she was to have graduated from Walnut Hills High School, a top fifty public high school in all of the country.

---

[1] All materials bracketed by quotation marks used herein are direct quotes from original sources, whether newspaper articles, my tape-recorded interviews with individuals, police interviews, trial transcripts, and the like.

In that year, 2001, Leah Marcus was one of 15,980 murder victims in the United States. The city of Cincinnati, Ohio, where the murdered occurred, experienced fifty-five murders. Cincinnati also had its share of forcible rapes that year, 358 reported.

Leah's death might otherwise have been a mere footnote to a list of senseless tragedies that the nation and its families experienced, but for the fact that it occurred at an explosive time in the city's sometimes explosively violent history, that of the riots of April 2001.

Leah was killed on Thursday, April 12, two months before her high school graduation, during the fourth day of those infamous race riots that racked Cincinnati that year. The riots made national, even international, news and were the largest civic disturbance in the U.S. since the Rodney King riots in Los Angeles in 1992. The riots blew open after years of simmering race relations in the city came to a head when a Cincinnati police officer, Stephen Roach, shot and killed an unarmed nineteen-year-old African American male, Timothy Thomas, in the predominantly African American community of Over-the-Rhine, just north of the city's central business district. A long history of police brutality against blacks and racial profiling boiled over with the death of Mr. Thomas. From April 9 through 13, the riots paralyzed the city and yielded opportunities for crimes ranging from beatings, lootings, robberies, and, with Leah's death, perhaps even murder.

Leah Marcus's boyfriend, Damon Allbright, was an eighteen-year-old classmate of Leah's, the son of a preacher, gifted singer, and star point guard for the Walnut Hills Eagles basketball team. He is also African American. Ultimately, and soon after the murder, he would become the police's prime suspect in Leah's death.

So it was against the background of the race riots, themselves to be overshadowed soon by the even more incendiary events of the summer of 2001, 9/11, that Leah's death and the investigation of her murder played out. For a period of time that spring and summer, other than the riots themselves, the Marcus death, its own microcosm of sex, murder, race, religion, and class, gripped the city of Cincinnati like no other story.

Leah was the younger of two children of Ben and Sarah Marcus. She had an older brother, David, who was a sophomore at the University of Chicago. Both Sarah and Ben Marcus were highly educated, successful, and rich individuals, themselves the products of successful Cincinnati families. Sarah is the CEO of Greater Cincinnati Wellsprings, a non-profit agency that assists mentally ill individuals, the daughter of the rabbi of Cincinnati's largest Jewish Reform congregation. Ben Marcus is a world-famous trial lawyer, the self-professed "Master of Disaster" or sometimes the "Prince of Torts," who headed a firm that handled class action lawsuits that yielded millions in fees. He was, next to Carl Lindner, who was the only person from Cincinnati ever to join the billionaire club, one of the richest men in the area, with a net worth in excess of half a billion dollars.

Damon Allbright was one of six children of the Reverend Othello Allbright, pastor of the Mt. Carmel Baptist Church, and his wife, Delores, herself a preacher's daughter. The fact that the mothers of the victim and the prime suspect were themselves children of clergymen was one of the interesting minor facts of the case and the source of much gossip. Mt. Carmel was not the largest congregation in Cincinnati, but one of the most influential, its leaders having been in the forefront of the Civil Rights era and the unofficial bully pulpit for the African American community's stance on the city's race relations. The Allbrights, like the Marcuses, lived in a leafy community of the city called North Avondale, only a few miles from downtown, home to Xavier University.

Cincinnati has fifty-two neighborhoods, and North Avondale is one of them centrally located between downtown and the northern edge of the city. North Avondale, according to its neighborhood association, "encompasses an area of approximately 1.3 square miles." Three quarters of the population is black, the rest mostly white. Bounded on the east by Victory Parkway near Xavier University, on the south by Glenwood, on the west by Vine Street, and on the north by East Mitchell, almost 6,000 people call North Avondale home. The median income is $30,000, just a few dollars more than the average household income throughout the city. Nonetheless, some very rich people live in some beautiful, expensive, and architecturally significant homes, including those of the Queen Anne, Victorian, Italian Renaissance, English Medieval, and Greek Revival styles, many built in the period between 1890 and 1930.

The USA is a nation born of violence and war and whose midwife was the indiscriminate shedder of blood. Cincinnati is no stranger to that legacy. The city is first and foremost a river city. Originally settled by white people around the protection of Fort Washington, the namesake fort still bears the name of a major traffic artery in town. The fort was erected across the Ohio River from the spot where the Licking River, which separates the cities of Newport and Covington, Kentucky, empties into the Ohio. The original founders named the fledgling city after the Roman citizen-soldier hero, Cincinnatus. But before it acquired that name, the settlement was known as Losantiville, a hodge-podge name derived from Latin meaning "the city at the mouth of the river," meaning the mouth of the Licking River.

In the 1700s, the American waterways were the equivalent of today's interstate highways, moving people and commerce around the country. A not uncommon, unsettling sight for some of those first settlers was the scalped bodies of their fellow colonists and water tinged red from the blood of those white people murdered by Native Americans as revenge for the theft of their land. The history of European settlement of this continent is replete with violence, death, and destruction. Cincinnati itself sits in the basin of a large river valley, hemmed in by, again borrowing from Roman legend, seven hills. At first, those hills proved a formidable barrier to the expansion of the city. But industrial might, and inclined streetcars, helped pave the expansion up and over that first tier of hills surrounding the valley.

As the population of the city swelled in the early 1800s, people migrated out of the river basin and up the hills into what were then the suburbs, and the village of Avondale sprang into existence. "Avon" is the Celtic word for river and "dale" refers to a valley. Oddly, there is neither a river in North Avondale nor a valley. In fact, the neighborhood rests at one of the higher elevations of the entire city. Later, it would be annexed into the city of Cincinnati and eventually renamed North Avondale, in deference to a community slightly to its south, just plain Avondale. When originally settled and subdivided, large tracts of land were developed for people of wealth to build stately homes. Some of these famous people included Barney Kroger, founder of still the country's largest grocery store chain, Kroger; Andrew Erkenbrecher, founder of the Cincinnati Zoo, which is bounded on one side by the eponymously named street; Frank Herschede, of the Herschede Clock Company; Samuel Pogue, of Pogue's Department Store; and Robert Mitchell, furniture magnate.

The architect, Samuel Hannaford, designed the Mitchell house in 1893. Mitchell actually built the home for his son, Richard. Hannaford is best remembered for some jewels of Cincinnati architecture, such as city hall and Music Hall. City hall was built over five years and completed the same year the Mitchell house was built. In 1893, Cincinnati's denizens paid $1,860,000 for their new municipal governing building. In today's dollars, that would be almost $50,000,000; although, that figure doesn't do justice to the intricacies of the building dating from a time when labor costs were much cheaper than would be available today.

Robert Mitchell emigrated to the United States from Ireland in 1829, apprenticed as a cabinetmaker, and eventually struck out on his own, establishing a partnership with Frederick Rammelsberg, one of thousands of Germans who migrated to Cincinnati. Many of these families lived in a neighborhood just north of the Miami and Erie Canal in the city center, which has since been filled in and paved and is now known as Central Parkway; that area is still known today as Over-the-Rhine. Mitchell and Rammelsberg furniture, known for rosewood, mahogany, and walnut wood with elaborate carvings, often of animals, is still widely collected today. Their partnership lasted until the end of the 1800s.

Mr. Mitchell's home, located at 9 Burton Woods Lane, sits on just over a half-acre parcel of land. Richard and his wife, Mary, donated the house to the Archdiocese of Cincinnati, which later deeded the home to a Montessori school in 1970. The school outgrew the premises and put the home on the market in the 1980s.

In between the times when the Archdiocese owned the house and the Montessori school did, the neighborhood of North Avondale changed its composition. After World War II, many of the old, rich families that lived there moved farther out into the suburbs and middle-class African Americans who lived in Avondale migrated to the stately area. Unlike other parts of the city that suffered what some referred to as "white flight," property values remained stable, homes were maintained, and the neighborhood retained its basic connotation as a nice place to live and raise a family.

When the Mitchell house finally became available to the public again, a thirty-six-year-old lawyer named Ben Marcus and his thirty-five-year-old wife, Sarah, purchased the home in 1985 for their expanding family. The Mitchell house is built completely of stone. It stands three stories tall, has a turret on the left front and a covered, arched porch with a balustrade. The roof is slate and, other than where the turret stands, has numerous gables.

The home has fireplaces with mantels in every room, Victorian woodwork throughout, as well as dramatic staircases. Hardwood floors are left open and warm in some rooms, covered with expensive Oriental carpets in others.

On April 12, Walnut Hills High School, in a part of town not far from the riots, cancelled school. Leah stayed home, ostensibly working on homework. Sarah left work early that day, to avoid any chance of being caught away from home after dark with a riot going on, and found her daughter dead on one of those expensive Oriental carpets in her very own bedroom.

Chapter Two

Last Date

On Saturday, April 7, 2001, seventeen-year-old Leah Marcus had less than eight weeks of high school left before she graduated and less than five full days of life left to live. Most people who knew her called her pretty; she didn't have classic beauty, a former classmate and one of her best friends recalled about her, because "her nose was too big," offered Tory Maxwell, appraising her friend's appearance. "But she was hot." Leah stood a mere five feet three inches tall, with long, wavy dark brown hair, liquid brown eyes, and an infectious smile that would "light up any room she entered," recalled Tory. Leah was witty, funny, talented and her goal in life was to become a pediatric neurosurgeon. Surgery, she knew, required impressive eye-hand coordination. As a talented, almost prodigy-like, piano player, Leah's signature piece was the complicated Franz Liszt "Hungarian Rhapsody #2," so she figured she had the chops to do vascular or neurosurgery.

Her next-door neighbor, Rebecca Stonecraft, told me that on spring evenings, she would sit outside on her porch just to listen to Leah practicing in her first-floor music room on the Steinway baby grand piano that Ben Marcus purchased specially for his talented daughter. The music wafted out of the open windows, filling the neighborhood with cheery sound. Sometimes other neighbors would stop by to chat and sit on Rebecca's porch listening to Leah's moonlight serenades, while enjoying a glass of lemonade or sweet tea.

Rebecca's family lived in the neighborhood ten years before the Marcuses moved in, and she was eight years older than Sarah Marcus. Rebecca and her husband had two children older than David and Leah, but nonetheless the families shared a kindred neighborliness and stayed close, before and after Leah's murder. Rebecca recalled how Leah started to learn the Liszt piece when she was fourteen. "It took her more than a year to master that piece. I would sit on the porch and listen to her practice and practice over and over again. Inevitably, she would come to a part she couldn't handle and slam her hands on the keys in frustration. But a second later, she would pick up the sequence from the place right before her error and do it again and again until she got it right. It was magic listening to her tame a piece of music. When she got it right, she would finish the sequence with a little flourish of trills."

At 10:00 a.m. on April the seventh, Leah put on jeans and a white top, hopped into her 1996 Volvo 850, and set out on her errands for the day. Her first stop was the home of a childhood friend, Bobby Evans, someone she attended school with since kindergarten. Bobby is a Downs syndrome person, but functions well enough to hold down a job, and lives independently with his wife, Sue, another Downs person, whom he met working at Goodwill. Leah described Bobby to many as her best friend; she always protected him from the bullies at school, even in first grade. She made a sensation in 2000 by inviting and taking Bobby as her date to the junior prom. Bobby recalled that last visit from his friend, the Saturday before her death. "We worked on a jigsaw puzzle. She always helped me with puzzles." Bobby's sense of loss for his friend is profound. "Why would anyone hurt Leah? I miss her." Sentiments as those were echoed many times in my conversations with people who knew Leah.

Her next visit was to Mitchell's hair salon downtown where she went monthly to get her hair done. On occasion, her mother would buy her a spa package for a massage or a manicure, pedicure, and a facial. Leah had a date scheduled that night with her boyfriend, Damon, and she wanted to look her best. They were going to a concert at Bogart's, a small-venue club in Clifton near the University of Cincinnati. Leah's tastes in music were eclectic; while she played Classical music, she loved listening to indie rock, jazz, classic rock, and country. I interviewed Leah's long-term stylist, Jennifer, who told me she had done Leah's hair for about three years. She, too, recalled a vibrant, bubbly teen who matured before her very eyes into a young woman set on going to medical school. Jennifer knew that Leah was a talented piano player. She once asked Leah why she wanted to become a doctor. Leah told her, "I know I can bring joy to people with my music. But how much more joy can I bring to the world by saving a child for his family?" Leah's preference to serve the community left a lasting impression on Jennifer.

After her visit to Mitchell's, Leah ate lunch downtown and then travelled to the riverfront area, including Sawyer's Point and Yeatman's Cove. She went alone, her mother told me, as she was wont to do on occasion. I asked Sarah Marcus why her daughter would visit the riverfront by herself so frequently. She replied, "Leah liked the river." One cannot live, be born and bred in Cincinnati without being aware that, at its core, this city is a river town. The mighty Ohio flows past on its infinite journey to the Mississippi, passing small towns and big cities from Pittsburgh to Cairo, Illinois. Perhaps Leah thought about the Native Americans who first plied the river in their canoes, at a time when the river was narrower, shallower, not gerrymandered by a series of dams installed to control flooding as well as river traffic. Or perhaps she mused about the possibility of escaping her life, using the metaphor of a river as a clarion call to action.

In talking to Leah's friends, family, schoolmates, and acquaintances, I found no one who spoke ill of Leah. Universally liked and loved, I wondered, what must it be like for a young woman, a teenager no less, and we all know how insecure and awkward teens can be, to feel such widespread approbation? Did she stride the earth with goodwill to all and not a hint of darkness that most of us remember from that age? Did she ever look at the rolling Ohio River and wonder, what would it be like just to jump in and sink to the bottom? Did she ever stand there on a moonlit night, the water still as marble, and contemplate the pull of that dark place, the eclipsing of the moon's rays as she descended to the bottom, never to resurface?

After her trip to the riverfront, she returned home and spent two hours practicing at the piano. Her mother was home the whole afternoon and remembers hearing her play; though, when I interviewed her years later, could no longer recall the pieces Leah practiced. She spent another two hours working on a school paper and then readied herself for her date with Damon.

Damon picked her up at seven, just as the elder Marcuses themselves were leaving to go out for dinner. Leah and Damon had tickets to see The Fab Four, a Beatles tribute band. The concert began at eight. The last song the band played was "Yesterday," sadly, only a few of which such days were left in Leah's young life.

Damon dropped Leah off back at her home a little before midnight. Sarah Marcus had returned with her husband by then and stayed up reading a book in the library, waiting for Leah to return home. It was the last time Damon would see Leah alive, he later told the police. As to those dark places? Sarah Marcus had a glimpse of them.

Known to none but Damon, Leah, and then Sarah when Leah told her, Leah did have secrets, deep dark ones, after all. In August, she would be heading to Cambridge to begin her freshman year at Harvard. Damon would attend the University of Cincinnati. Leah liked Damon, but he was not the love of her life. She had too much to see and explore before settling down with one man, she told her mother. She would have to sever her relationship with Damon before she left, and she had, in fact, told him that night that she was breaking up with him. This fact Sarah Marcus made sure to let the detectives know about when they came to investigate Leah's murder.

Chapter Three

Driving while Black

Timothy Thomas had nothing in common with Leah other than that he, too, died, a victim of homicide while still a teenager. He was, at the time that Leah and Damon took their seats at Bogart's, already dead for eighteen hours, having been shot to death in an Over-the-Rhine alley by Patrolman Stephen Roach at 2:20 a.m. that very morning.

Thomas's mother, Angela Leisure, called her son "Tim," and I will do so in this book. Tim Thomas's life could not have been more different than Leah Marcus's. He grew up poor and African American in the Over-the-Rhine neighborhood just north of the city's central business district, bordered on the south by Central Parkway. A long time ago, Central Parkway wasn't a road at all; it was part of the Miami and Erie Canal system that linked the Ohio River with Lake Erie at the north end of the state at Toledo. The iron horse, the railroad, put most of the canals out of business. In Cincinnati, the canal was eventually paved over and became Central Parkway. But as the city expanded to the north of the canal, many immigrants from Germany settled there, having to cross the few bridges that linked the neighborhood with the central city to the south.

To the German immigrants, the canal reminded them of the Rhine River, and hence the neighborhood became known as *über den Rhein* in German, or more colloquially as Over-the-Rhine.

Over-the-Rhine consists of three areas, with a north-south bifurcation at Liberty Street. North of Liberty are the areas known as the Northern Liberties and the Brewery District. Given the influx of Germans in the nineteenth century, beer was sure to follow. Cincinnati had a grand history of brewing and much of it came out of the Brewery District. Christian Moerlein opened his brewery in 1853. In the 1800s, hundreds of beer gardens called Over-the-Rhine home. As his beer found success and a national market, Moerlein's operation expanded unto three complete city blocks. Prohibition put the breweries out of business. The Washington Park area, now known as the Gateway Quarter, lies just north of Central Parkway. The park sits across Elm Street from Music Hall. This area has been the subject of much gentrification, which caused many of the African Americans and other poor white people, often of Appalachian heritage, who long lived there, since after World War II, to relocate further afield and into other parts of Over-the-Rhine.

Tim's funeral was in Over-the-Rhine at the New Prospect Baptist Church. His son Tywon three months old at the time, attended. Tim and Tywon's mother, Monique Crutchfield (Wilcox at the time of the shooting), never married; although, after Tim died, she married another man. Perhaps, had he lived, Tim and Monique would have gotten married.

Tim grew up poor, in a neighborhood where the annual income barely exceeded $8,000 a year, far less than the $26,000 annual income of a Cincinnati resident and much less than the $30,000 the typical North Avondale resident earned. Those numbers seem paltry compared with the $55,000 average for the thirteen counties surrounding Cincinnati that constitute the metropolitan statistical area known as Greater Cincinnati. Tim's family earnestly denies that he was involved in the drug trade, a common enough assumption on the part of Cincinnati police officers who view unemployed young African Americans as drug dealers by way of default, guilty until proven innocent.

Tim may have been a not atypical youth who grew up poor where the prospects for employment were dismal. He may have been restless and bored, but not violent and not a criminal. Tywon's favorite story about his father was that his parents liked to argue. Monique would tell Tywon that Tim would finish the argument with the line, "Your dad said I could have anything I wanted if we broke up. But he was keeping Tywon."

Tim was turning his life around. Though he did not graduate from high school, he earned a GED. He applied for and accepted a job through a temporary service. He aspired to a career in electronics. His new job was to have started two days after he died.

Like a lot of young African American men in Cincinnati at that time, and for decades before, Tim's biggest crime was "driving while black." By April 7, 2001, in a mere two months, Tim had racked up twenty-one misdemeanor traffic charges, none for an actual moving violation. His tickets were for driving without a seat belt or driving without a license. Tim's mom, Angela, recalls having had more than one conversation with her son to "just get your license; wake up."

What is problematic about Tim's tickets is, as noted above, they were all non-moving violations. If you run a red light, or rear-end somebody, and a police officer is around, you will get a ticket and you will get points on your license. This is expected; it's a moving violation. The officer has probable cause to believe that an offense has been committed. If you also fail to wear a seat belt and drive without a license, then you will get charged with those offenses as well.

On the other hand, if the "probable cause" charge is driving without a seat belt, then the officer has to be looking very hard at the driver even to spot this infraction. What actually happens is that the officers in Tim's cases, and of the eleven traffic stops, he was pulled over by six different white officers and four black ones, are actually suspecting Tim, and hundreds of young men like him, of being involved in the drug trade. When asked if her son was a drug dealer, Angela replied, that if he was, "he was the brokest one you would ever meet."

Driving while black is but one of the countless indignities that people of color deal with in a predominantly white America. The simplest things that, to me, as a white woman, seem obvious, are different for people of color. Black people are perceived by whites as dangerous. When fear gets in the way, an inclination to shoot first and ask questions later follows. As I interviewed black men and women for this book, I heard countless examples of those indignities. A black man told me he had seen whites, men and women, cross the street when he was walking on the same sidewalk, just to get away from him. It didn't matter if he was walking his pit bull or just alone. They were afraid of him, a harmless aerospace engineer who worked at the GE jet engine plant in Evendale.

A black woman told me she went into a beauty supply store with her two little girls in tow, and the owner followed her around from aisle to aisle, inquiring if he could help her, but ostensibly making sure that she didn't steal anything. "Why would he assume I was there to steal?" she asked me. "I have no record; I have my five- and seven-year-old daughters with me. What kind of example would I be setting for them by stealing? Why did he assume, if I didn't ask for any help, he would ask me if I needed any? He didn't ask the white women who came into the store if they needed any help."

I had another woman tell me the story when she parked her car one summer day in the parking lot of her own apartment complex. A middle-aged white man walked up to her as she got out of her car. He complained that he thought she almost ran him over when she had not. She had her small children in the car, and the only thing on her mind was getting them all home safe and unpacking the groceries. Nevertheless, she felt compelled to apologize, even though she hadn't done anything wrong. Then he tells her if he had a gun, he would have shot her, and why don't you just go home to whatever country you are from. She's an American; born and bred right here in the Midwest.

Her great-great grandfather was a slave, and this gentleman would tell his family a story about police brutality, comparing it to what life was like in the South following the Civil War, after Lincoln freed the slaves. He used to say, "They took off their robes, and they gave them badges," explaining how white racists morphed from the Klan into cops.

A little after midnight on April the seventh, Tim seemed to have been a changed man. He had a job he was going to start on Monday. He had an infant son and lived with the boy and his mother, taking responsibility for the new life he helped to create. He set out from his apartment at 1319 Republic Street, just two short blocks from Music Hall, the part of Over-the-Rhine, which, even then, was starting to gentrify. With less than two hours to live, he told Monique he was heading to a convenience store to buy some cigarettes. He never made it home alive.

Chapter Four

Days of Outrage and Carnage

This work is fact based. I have committed to pursuing and expounding the truth, with my own foibles, prejudices, and biases left out. So, excuse this one maudlin moment of conjecture involving Tim Thomas. I would like to think, with no proof as to the verity of the assumption, that when Tim left his apartment early in the morning of April 7, 2001, that he kissed his girlfriend and infant son goodbye and told them that he loved them. His tragic death, otherwise, would forever leave lingering doubts in their minds as to his love and appreciation for them.

What we do know is that after he left the store with his cigarettes, he was spotted on the street by off-duty patrol officers working security who recognized Tim as a person with outstanding *capiases*, or bench warrants, issued by the Hamilton County Municipal Court for failing to appear when summoned to answer for the infractions for which he had been ticketed. It was after midnight, dark downtown, and in a moment of fear, Tim ran when the officers approached him. The officers radioed for assistance and gave chase.

For ten minutes, Tim, a tall, lanky young man, outran nine police officers through the streets and alleys of Over-the-Rhine. But then he made the unintended, and fatal, mistake of turning into an alley at 13th and Republic Streets, a mere half block from his apartment. Inside that dark, litter-strewn alley with graffiti spray-painted on the walls, Tim ran into Patrolman Stephen Roach.

When Tim rounded the corner, he surprised Roach. The officer ordered Tim to stop and surrender. They say there are two sides to every story. The only story we will ever hear as to what took place that night is Stephen Roach's story, which he explained in detail later when tried for the killing of Timothy Thomas. Tim made no statements to first responders or medical personnel; within an hour of being shot in the chest, he died at the hospital. There were no surveillance cameras in that alley. No other spectators with cell phones were present to video the confrontation. Cell-phone picture technology wasn't available commercially until 2002, and video appeared even later than that. Bodycams for police officers had yet to be invented.

According to Roach, Tim Thomas failed to comply with his order to stop and, further, reached into the "baggy" waistband of his pants. Roach believed that Tim was reaching for a gun, and in that split second, when instant decisions have to be made that will forever alter the lives of police officers and suspects alike, Roach shot Thomas in what the officer maintained was self-defense. One bullet to the chest, near the heart, was all that was needed to snuff out the life of an unarmed young man whose fatal mistake was to attempt to pull his pants up rather than put his arms in the air.

Prosecutors will tell you that one of the hardest cases they have to handle are officer-involved shootings. No one ever wins one of these cases. Juries traditionally empathize with the police officers who have a split second to make a life and death decision. Most juries tend to give the officer the benefit of the doubt, and so the vast majority of these cases end with a hung jury. Most of the people shot by police officers are criminals and/or engaged in criminal behavior at the moment of the shooting. That said, there have been far too many stories of questionable shootings of unarmed black men, any one of which is a tragedy and a wrong, which society should not sanction.

Stephen Roach, given the high-profile optics of his case, chose not to exercise his right to trial by jury. He was tried before a judge, a bench trial, and found not guilty of negligent homicide. Unlike Tim Thomas, Roach had the option of which high-stakes forum he would choose to determine his fate.

No report of Tim's death was mentioned in the Saturday morning edition of the *Cincinnati Tribune*; stories published for that edition had already been written and edited, and the presses ran. Today's online version of the newspaper didn't exist then. But I was roused at 3:00 a.m. by a source in the police department that something big was happening in Over-the-Rhine. In less than an hour, I had dressed, driven downtown, and ran into a phalanx of police officers who cordoned off the area, while the crime technicians completed their work. Detectives working the case were tight-lipped and spouted nothing other than facts: Timothy Thomas, age nineteen. Officer Stephen Roach, four-year veteran of the police department. No known witnesses. Reaching for a gun. Fired in self-defense. The usual tropes fed to a reporter without acknowledging the larger issues at hand, of which the police department and its very members were quite cognizant of in April 2001.

The shooting was, however, by Sunday, April 8, front page, and the lead article in the *Tribune*. My article. By then, I had most of a day to work the case and, within the constraints of a reporter's duty, blandly collated what little was known. Officer Roach went in pursuit after a radio call for help. Multiple warrants for misdemeanors. Roach placed on paid administrative leave. The grieving girlfriend interviewed. The Fraternal Order of Police president interviewed, asking for calm pending the results of the investigation. The Cincinnati Black United Front indicated it would protest at 3:00 p.m. the next day at city hall. The ACLU filed a lawsuit on behalf of the CBUF three weeks previously, alleging a pattern of racial profiling and police brutality against African Americans. Roach shot Thomas just five months after the death of another black man, Roger Owensby Jr., who died in a police chokehold, while the police tried to arrest him.

These bland facts, publicly reported, lay bare and sober compared to the maelstrom brewing among Cincinnati's African American community. While no report of the shooting made the Saturday morning paper, by the time the sun was up on the morning of Saturday the seventh, the initial calls went out along the grapevine of the affected community. Delores Allbright, Damon's mother and Othello's wife, told me that, like I was, she was awakened early that Saturday morning. A congregant who lived in Over-the-Rhine and knew of the shooting called the Allbright house to inform Othello. This man pleaded with Othello to come downtown right away, which he did.

Some residents of the African American community pleaded for calm, but others' voices would not be silenced. Since 1995, Cincinnati police officers killed fifteen black men, including Tim Thomas. Race relations had been dubious for decades before Tim's death, but a section of the community had reached the end of its complacency. The rapidity with which African American suspects kept dying in confrontations with the police accelerated; five alone in the six months preceding Tim's death. Members of the black community felt that the city's government ignored their concerns, too busy spending time building sports stadiums for the rich white owners of professional sports teams with no time to spare for the problems of day-to-day life in poor, urban neighborhoods.

By Monday, April 9, a city hall filled with loud protestors would host a city council meeting that would long be remembered in Cincinnati. But the day before, Sunday, I found myself downtown again, in that alley at 13th and Republic Streets. The police were gone, the bloodstains hosed away. A makeshift memorial, of the type all too often seen then and since, had sprung up. Pictures of Tim, candles, and flowers lay among the detritus in that alley. Someone had spray painted "RIP TiM" on the rear of the building near where the young man lay bleeding the day before. Try as I would, I never did ascertain why the graffiti artist put a small "i" in Tim when all the other letters were capitalized.

Delores Allbright had been prescient when she related to me after the fact that days of outrage would begin. She said that both she and Othello were proud to lead the chorus. But, as whenever mobs get involved, things spin out of control. Soon, the days of outrage would lead to days of carnage.

Chapter Five

Councils and Circuses

Al Gerhardstein filed the lawsuit in March 2001 on behalf of the Cincinnati Black United Front and the Ohio ACLU alleging police misconduct. Gerhardstein is a Cincinnati institution among civil rights lawyers. He has a long history of standing up for the powerless. His most famous case is *Obergefell v. Hodges*, the 2015 Supreme Court case that legalized gay marriage as a constitutional right throughout the fifty states.

In the run-up to filing his police case, he spent a lot of time with members of the African American community. Clearly, there was a disconnect between what black and white members of the public saw and felt when interacting with police. African Americans told him they were scared of the police. That the police stuck guns in their faces. They were terrified of the police. The police were corrupt.

The suit highlighted contentious issues, such as police pulling over black motorists, or even pedestrians, pushing them to the ground, handcuffing them, and holding them for unreasonable periods of time. Officers used abusive language to the detainees, hoping to provoke them into a reaction that would then be used to charge them with a crime, such as disorderly conduct or resisting arrest. The police charged blacks, who made up forty-three percent of the population, with eighty percent of the infractions, such as driving without a license, without insurance, without a seat belt, or jaywalking.

Like many cities, police supervisors in Cincinnati judge officers on how many arrests they make. They are commended for high quotas and disciplined for low ones. They find it easier to arrest poor, minority people, folks who are less likely to fight charges in court. Once in the criminal justice system, they find representation from the public defender's office, whose lawyers have hundreds of cases on their plates. They urge clients to plea bargain to a lesser offense. These lawyers are known derisively by their nickname, "public pretenders."

Henry James, 26, said, "I've been harassed by the same police officer who killed Thomas. He jumps out of his patrol car and chases people down all the time. When are they going to do something about this mess around here? They're not protecting the community; and the black police are just as bad as the white police officers. Hamilton County Prosecutor Mike Allen has never prosecuted any police officer for killing someone. They just suspend the police officers, and eventually, it dies out. Instead, they want to prosecute us for rioting and violating the curfew. In Cincinnati, there is no chance of life getting better. It's going to go back to the same thing.

They'll turn around and do the same thing in six months from now."

Shawn, who declined to give his last name, 24, said, "I've been beat up by the police for no apparent reason. One time, I was coming out of the building, and they grabbed me and began choking me by the neck. I was scared that they're trying to hurt me, so I broke away, but I didn't get far. They maced me and put me in handcuffs and in the back seat of their car. I'm back there telling them I didn't do anything. The police officer told me to shut up, so I told him to shut up, and he maced me again. They took me down to the justice center, and they whipped me there too."

This disconnect was obvious when I spoke with members of the force or other white citizens. The officers denied bias. They complained that no one appreciated the difficulty and dangers of their jobs. Of those fifteen black men killed by police between 1995 and 2001, plenty of them were dangerous felons, some armed, who had attacked, and even killed, police officers. Harvey Price, who holds the distinction of being the first of those fifteen victims of police gunfire, axed his girlfriend's fifteen-year-old daughter to death, then held a SWAT team at bay for four hours before attacking officers with a knife. He was shot dead. Jermaine Lowe, wanted on a parole violation for armed robbery, fled in a stolen car, was chased by the police, smashed into another car, and exited his vehicle firing his weapon. He, too, was gunned down in a hail of police bullets. Widows of police officers and Fraternal Order of Police union leaders went on talk shows and wrote letters to the editor to express their support for the hard and dangerous work of their slain husbands and co-workers.

Public anger grew. Protestors took to invading city hall with their message. They shouted down council meetings. They carried fake coffins around and wore shirts splattered with fake blood. One man who lived in Avondale told me that it had been like this since Martin Luther King got shot over thirty years before. "Nothing had changed and nothing never would," he opined. Except that this time, he was wrong.

Council met on Monday to demand from the city manager and the police chief an explanation of what happened with the Thomas shooting. Over two hundred people, including Tim's mother, Angela Leisure, gathered outside waiting to hear the results. When advised by spectators that no answers were forthcoming, multiple individuals stormed into the chambers of the council to demand their own explanation.

This group included the Special Forces, a group of black nationalists known for spewing anti-white and anti-Semitic diatribes; ordinary citizens, Othello Allbright, Tim Thomas's mother and the attorney she had already hired, Ken Lawson, who then was making a name for himself. Lawson himself is African American. He started out his legal career working in one of the bastions of white-shoe law firms, Taft, Stettinius, & Hollister, but soon found his interests lay elsewhere. He would champion black people and their causes. He was, in some ways, Cincinnati's answer to Johnny Cochrane. He became a serious and effective criminal defense lawyer in the 1990s and early 2000s, defending celebrities like Deion Sanders and the common man alike. He made the cover of *Cincinnati* magazine dressed in a full-length leather coat walking two pit bull dogs on leashes.

He represented Deion Sanders in a case where he was charged (while playing for the Cincinnati Reds) with dragging a police officer on his scooter after being ordered to stop for an alleged traffic violation. The jury acquitted Sanders. That case brought Lawson's name into prominence, but the Cincinnati riots and his bellicose tone at the city council meeting, which ultimately led to a $12 million settlement (without ever having to go to trial), made him a superstar among Cincinnati attorneys.

John Cranley, then a rookie council member and some years later mayor himself, described a surreal environment for one of his first meetings. The crowd was loud, screaming, and he felt uncomfortable and unsafe. The scene was more circus than city council meeting. The room was filled with hundreds of people; there was no way even to turn around. Protestors occupied every inch of floor space. Every corner of the room, even the area behind the seats of the very council members, teemed with angry, yelling citizens. The noise, the body heat, the protest signs with slogans that read, "Stop killing us...or else!", all combined to turn a forum of democratic rule into a circus of mob politics.

The mood inside council chambers was not only somber but tense and charged. The undulations of the mob's anger were cleverly manipulated by one of the main characters of this story. Othello Allbright masterfully inflamed the crowd by suggesting that city officials were withholding information about the Thomas shooting. (The legitimacy of such an argument is dubious because investigations into police shootings typically take many months. Additionally, council itself wanted answers so that it could account to the citizenry; if nothing else, it was the politically expedient thing to do.) He threatened to hold the chambers hostage until Roach's after-action statements about what happened were released. Probably he knew that such an early disclosure might jeopardize any efforts to subsequently try Patrolman Roach for the shooting death of Tim Thomas.

"You took a part of my life. I demand to know why," Angela Leisure challenged the elected officials of city government. I read that quote in the *Enquirer* when it came out in April of 2001. I reread it again ten years later when I decided to start writing this book. What I missed then, but see now, is how the white reporter captured the image of the "angry black woman" "demanding to know why," yet didn't write about the pain and hurt she felt over losing a son, cut down in the prime of his life for no reason other than a white officer feigned fear at the sight of an unarmed black man in an alley. Where was the story of her loss? Her grief? Her humanity?

Council tried to assuage the crowd by explaining they would push for a change to police hiring practices, even as to the hiring of the police chief. The crowd's jeering response clearly expressed its opinion that it was not

44

mollified. No answers came, and for three hours, the protestors refused to leave without getting direct answers.

Allbright threatened to have the doors to the chambers barred. John Cranley, Chair of the Law Committee, took the opportunity to leave during a brief recess. He hoped that doing so would calm the crowd. Members of the crowd pushed and shoved him as he left the council chambers. Visibly shaken, he returned after the recess and resorted to banging his gavel, calling for order when none, obviously, could be found. The crowd responded by chanting that "the police should be put in order!" Council member Alicia Reese, herself African American, demanded that the mayor, the city manager, John Shirey, and the police chief, Tom Streicher, all appear and account to the citizenry. The crowd surrounded the dais where the members sat, even surging behind them. They stood on desks, they shoved chairs out of their way, they yelled from the balcony overlooking the floor. When Chief Streicher finally appeared, they moved right up behind him. So concerned were his officers that three of them placed their bodies between him and the crowd, forming a blue barricade, so the chief could address the council without overt concern of being assaulted himself. He started his explanation that he could not release any details because of the pending investigation. The crowd yelled its disbelief.

Three hours after the commencement of the meeting, Councilman Jim Tarbell finally gave the crowd something by way of explanation. The officer involved thought Tim might have had a gun. There was a videotape of part of the incident, but it had already been sealed by grand jury subpoena. Othello Allbright taunted the council that the explanation, that Thomas was pulling a gun out of his pants, just as easily could have changed had Thomas been apprehended in a car. Then, he said, the officer would have said that Tim was trying to run him over. With that explanation, though, meager that it was, Allbright allowed the council to adjourn provided that they "call off the dogs," meaning all the police officers assembled inside and outside the chambers and in the streets surrounding city hall.

The carnage began after sundown that night.

Chapter Six

Mayhem

After the city hall crowd dispersed, it did not disband. It marched several blocks north to police headquarters, also the site of the District One police station, diagonally across Central Parkway from Music Hall in Over-the-Rhine. The crowd's anger grew as it marched, voices strident, demanding a showdown with the police. The riot started with someone throwing a brick through the glass-paneled front door of police headquarters. Police on horseback and in cruisers confronted the crowd of several hundred people. Rocks and bottles flew at the officers and their steeds. Police responded with tear gas, rubber bullets, and beanbags fired from shotguns. The confrontation lasted about an hour. The police arrested ten people that night. In the face of this strong, albeit non-fatal response, the crowd backed off. But not before someone pulled the American flag down off the large pole in the yard in front of headquarters and re-strung it upside down. The perpetrator of this action may have known, or not, that his statement visually represented the topsy-turvy, upside down nature of justice in Cincinnati that spring.

On the next afternoon, Tuesday, April 10, rioting continued. A small crowd of fifty young men in Over-the-Rhine started moving down the streets, followed by a cordon of police officers. At several intersections, the crowd threw garbage and bottles at the police who retreated out of range. Some of the crowd split off and headed downtown where they overturned vendor carts, newspaper boxes, and garbage cans. The crowd grew in size and smashed windows of downtown businesses and began looting the stores of clothes, appliances, liquor, big screen TVs, whatever could be found. The mob even looted Findlay Market, the site of one of the major successes in the neighborhood, an indoor/outdoor market patronized by affluent whites from the suburbs.

Roving crowds of thugs stopped random motorists in the street, white motorists, dragged them from their cars, and beat them. They stood in the street, throwing bricks at passing vehicles, always vehicles driven by white people. WCPO, an ABC television affiliate, showed videotape on the late news of the mob pulling a Kentucky truck driver from his vehicle and beating him, shades of the Rodney King riots in Los Angeles almost a decade earlier. A WCPO reporter interviewed a woman, blood streaming down her face. She stated that the mob pulled her from her car, beat her, including striking her on the head with a brick, and that the crowd even dragged her elderly mother from the car and beat her, too. The rioters attacked, mistakenly, one of their own. Roslyn Jones, an Albino black person, was identified as "a white woman," and the crowd threw bricks at her. One black man recognized that she was a black person and yelled that information to the crowd to stop hurting her, while he pulled her to safety.

As police moved through Over-the-Rhine, protestors threw bottles out of apartment windows at them; those in the streets threw bricks and stones. Some officers reported shots fired at them, although, no injuries resulted.

Some in the crowd displayed homemade signs proclaiming, "Black Power" and "Honk if you're black." Again, the police moved in on horseback and on foot, with arms linked, forcing the rioters to disperse with tear gas and beanbags. The police arrested sixty-six people on Tuesday.

More riots broke out in adjacent, poor neighborhoods such as Avondale and Walnut Hills. The participants broke hundreds more windows and started fires. The authorities called in Hamilton County Sheriff's deputies to assist the Cincinnati officers. When the sun went down, thugs fired shots, the crowd injured more bystanders, and the bedlam continued into the early morning hours of Wednesday, the eleventh of April. Of those arrested on Tuesday, most of them were young black males between the ages of eighteen and twenty-four.

The nature of the protests changed as day turned into night. During the day, peaceful protestors, including Othello Allbright, marched. Othello and other members of the clergy stood at the front of the crowd, acting as a human buffer between protestors and police, and encouraged peaceful demonstration. But as afternoon wore on and shadows grew long as the sunlight began to wane, the violent ones took over the streets. The rioters pushed beyond the boundaries of Over-the-Rhine and downtown. Westwood, Avondale, Norwood, Walnut Hills, and other communities felt the wrath of lawless bands of hoodlums. Hooligans fired more shots, one striking a Cincinnati police officer in his utility belt. "Shots fired; officer down," rang out over police radios throughout the city. Mayor Charlie Luken, when informed of this incident, and realizing that officers could not continue working twelve-hour shifts, considered bringing in the National Guard. The officer was not seriously injured due to the fortuitousness of the bullet striking him in his utility belt.

Just after 11:00 p.m., Cristina Clark, a nineteen-year-old African-American woman, stood behind the screen door of her home on Republic Street watching the violence erupting in Over-the-Rhine. Someone threw a bottle off a balcony, and it landed close to her. Then she heard what she thought was a firecracker but was actually an errant bullet. It clipped her right ear. Doctors sutured fifteen stitches in her ear to close the wound. "I'm scared to death," she told my *Tribune* colleague, "scared of being shot again. But I'm alive. That's all that matters." Just yards away from her screen door is the alley where Tim Thomas had died just a few days before.

Not far from Cristina's home, at the Bank Café at 12th and Vine, unwanted visitors entered the store and started stealing things. Khaled Daqeer tried to get the miscreants to leave, but someone hit him on the back of the head with a heavy object fracturing his skull. He lived to tell the story.

Mayor Luken holed up in city hall working with advisors, the police chief, lawyers, pastors, the Cincinnati Human Relations Council, anyone who could help effect an end to the violence. Later in the day, he left his office and headed to Over-the-Rhine in his official car to survey the situation. Protestors blocked the car's path and screamed insults at him, demanding he leave the area.

Long-time residents and visitors alike could not reconcile the scenes of violence with the quiet, midwestern city they knew. Shawn Wiegand told a reporter that he felt as if he landed in the Gaza Strip.

The next day, Thursday the twelfth, the mayor imposed an 8:00 p.m. curfew, and the situation, always volatile after sundown, started settling down. Soon, the clean-up and the cooldown would occur on city streets scarred by four days of violent protest. By Friday, Mayor Luken called in the National Guard. The riots wound down on Friday, coincidentally the day that Tim Thomas was buried.

Buried on Metro page two, on Friday the thirteenth, was my short article about a young woman killed in her own home in North Avondale on Thursday, April 12.

Chapter Seven

Last Days

Leah Marcus, after breaking up with her boyfriend on Saturday the seventh, returned to Walnut Hills High School on Monday, April 9. She attended only that day and the next. By Tuesday night, the school administration, concerned about the rioting in the city as a whole, and in the school's own neighborhood, cancelled classes starting Wednesday until further notice.

Leah's last two days in school started out uneventful. She attended the usual panoply of classes that the academically vigorous had access to at a college preparatory school like Walnut Hills. Her mother showed me her report cards some years later. She carried a 4.2 GPA throughout her high school career. Her third quarter grades put her tied, at that point, with one other girl to graduate as the valedictorian of the class. This other girl, Toni Bissonnette, graciously asked the school to award Leah the honor as valedictorian posthumously since no one knew what the final grades would have been.

Leah's last quarter of classes consisted of Advanced Placement English, Advanced Placement French, History, Chemistry, and Calculus. Her elective was Music, where she spent most of her time working on her piano craft, encouraged by Dr. Sarah Winters, who ran the music department at the school.

Winters, who I interviewed for this book some ten years after Leah's death, still recalled the "wow factor" (her words) that Leah presented. "She could have won a full-ride scholarship to Juilliard if she had wanted to. Even with all the money her parents had, Juilliard would have begged her to come." Winters didn't bother with Leah attending regular music classes. She gave her time to practice her music alone, while the rest of the class endured tedious repetitions *en masse*. Leah played keyboards in Walnut Hills musical productions, including electric keyboards. Winters started working with Leah on composition during her senior year, hoping to inspire the young woman to compose as well as to play. "She had confided in me that she wanted to become a doctor. A surgeon. I am never one to talk a child out of her dream, but the world would have lost a rare talent if she chose medicine over music. As it turned out, the world lost a rare talent no matter which vocation she would have pursued."

While Leah had broken up with Damon the previous Saturday night, no one outside of the immediate families knew this fact. Apparently, neither Leah nor Damon shared the news with any of their close friends. So when Leah returned to school on Monday morning, there was no schoolhouse gossip of the type that rips through the halls of a high school the way a fire sweeps through the dry tinder and timber of a forest in the middle of a three-year drought.

But by lunchtime on Monday, the chorus of gossip erupted in the dining hall. When I took a tour of Walnut Hills that summer, after school was out and I was following the trial proceedings for the *Tribune*, I visited the lunch hall. Walnut Hills High School inhabits its "current" building, which was erected in 1931. The floors are terrazzo, the ceilings high, a Monticello-like dome sits atop the roof, and six Corinthian columns hold up the portico to the entrance atop a concrete staircase. Like many of the public areas of the building (as opposed to the classrooms), the dining room has a high ceiling paved with acoustic tiles. I imagine those tiles do little to reduce the decibel level in the cafeteria during the lunch rush as hundreds of students jabber with each other. On my tour of the building, I marveled at the ceiling, from which hundreds of forks protruded from those tiles, having been launched into them at high velocity by students sitting at the tables below.

Leah ate lunch with Tory Maxwell, who was Leah's best friend from high school, and six other girls. When the lunch period was just about over, an African American student, Dante Braxton, a teammate of Damon's on the basketball team and Damon's best friend from school, came over to the girls' table. Dante is large for a high schooler, standing seventy-nine inches and weighing over 240 pounds; he projects power and confidence. (He went on to play college basketball at Georgetown University.) He played both football and basketball for the Eagles, as the high school's teams were denominated. Unlike a lot of basketball players, this man-child already had considerable bulk, which made him a perfect tight end for the football team and power forward for the basketball team. He is also one of those men, so tall, that people just get out of his way when he walks down the street or through the halls of a high school.

At seven inches over six feet tall, when he came over to Leah's table and stared down at her and her friends, the look could have gone either way. He could have been your big brother, stopping by to visit a younger sibling and check on you, or he could be an intimidating, downright scary specter towering over a tiny sixty-three-inch girl like Leah. His natural voice projects and booms, no doubt assisted by the prodigious lung capacity of an athlete. That day, according to Tory, he was not the protective, older sibling. He did not smile, and while his voice did not boom out, it was all the more sinister by the quiet way he delivered his message. Tory, Leah, and the girls almost had to strain to hear what he had to say over the din of the dining hall. Between the tone of voice and scowl on his face, Tory recalled, you would have had to be an idiot not to get the tenor of his message.

"Damon told me you broke it off with him. He's upset. Very upset. I think you should go over to him," and he pointed to where Damon sat with his group of friends on the far side of the cafeteria, "and tell him you've changed your mind. You'll take him back. Otherwise, he says, you'll be sorry."

The message was a threat, in Tory's mind, and there is but little doubt that it could be construed or intended as otherwise. It is also what the lawyers call hearsay, that is, an out-of-court statement offered for its truth. Generally, hearsay isn't admissible in trials, civil or criminal. But in Ohio, the Rules of Evidence allow a statement by a party (a plaintiff or defendant) that is deemed "an admission against interest." The lawyers would later wrangle over this exchange, which was ultimately deemed admissible in Damon's case. The materiality of this statement of Damon's, if Damon even made such a statement, which he denied, (Was it just a fabrication of Dante's? Was Dante just trying to help his friend out?), was crucial to the prosecution's case. It hinted at motive. Motive is not a technical element of a crime. The prosecution doesn't have to prove that a defendant had a particular motive in committing a crime. But motive goes a long way in explaining to a jury why a defendant committed a crime. Juries always want to know the reason behind the crime; motive is the prosecutor's friend and tool in illuminating that part of the story for the jury.

In any event, Dante's "threat" was duly noted by Leah's friends, and the gossip mill started spewing before the girls even got back to their after-lunch classes. Gossip has been a part of high school for generations. But, lately, it has gotten more and more caustic, especially with the revolution of smartphones and social media, both of which were in their infancy in 2001. Despite that, oral gossip works almost as well, if not as fast, as electronic gossip, with the obvious difference that what is spewed into cyberspace stays there forever, while that whispered in a friend's ear has a more fleeting life. By 2:30, as school was wrapping up that Monday, it seemed to Tory as if the whole school knew that Leah had dumped Damon. The gossip knives were being sharpened against the whetstone of the rumor mill.

Tory recalls that Leah drove herself to and from school, but Tory did not have a car and so she rode the bus home. She remembers that "everyone" on the bus peppered her with questions about Leah's breakup. The usual cruel words directed against young women were thrown at Leah, "whore" and "slut." The bus riders wanted to know from Tory who Leah had dumped Damon for, as if it was natural and assumed that she had already moved on to another boyfriend for a sexual relationship. Tory noted to me, as if it made some kind of difference, that the white girls on the bus spewed more vitriol even than the African American girls. When she arrived home, Tory called Leah and told her about the statements she overheard. She said Leah was upset. She was upset first and foremost that she was breaking up with Damon, who Leah said was the first love of her life. She was upset that people were gossiping about her. According to Tory, Leah found herself in a predicament that she wasn't used to being in. She was the object of vicious words and not gracious compliments and platitudes of what a fine young person she was and what great things she would do in the world. Leah confessed to Tory that she was hurt and thinking about skipping school the next day because she couldn't bear to deal with it face-to-face.

So Tory was surprised, at least a little, when Leah showed up at school the next morning. "Sort of, I guess," she said. "With Leah, you knew that even when something was tough, she wouldn't run away from it. She would just find a way to deal with it." The comments and slurs continued on Tuesday, so much so that Sarah Marcus, even years after her daughter's death, told me that Leah came home from school that day in tears from what she heard. Sarah knew a lot about the toll that bullying takes on young people; many of the clients of the non-profit she runs experienced bullying as children. Some of them ended up with mental health problems as a direct result of bullying. When I pressed Sarah Marcus to see if Leah complained about the race of the kids belittling her at school, Sarah would not take the bait. "It's not a race thing." Yet, of course, later, at Damon's trial, it was all about "the race thing." She continued, "Kids of both races treated her completely disrespectfully. No one bothered to want to hear her side of the story, the reason she broke up with Damon."

In 2001, the year someone murdered Leah, school bullying was hardly a new phenomenon. In the ensuing years, several high-profile cases of bullying rocked the greater Cincinnati area. A number of the victims ended up killing themselves. The Walnut Hills High

School newspaper, the *Chatterbox* (what an ironically gossipy name that is), printed five editorials about bullying in school. They appeared long after Leah's death. Even if they had shown up before, they would not have prevented her death. But they might have made her last few days of life a little more bearable. Other victims of school bullying chose other ways to deal with the subject. They morphed into many of the school shooters that have come along since Columbine.

On Wednesday the eleventh, Leah stayed cloistered at home. The Walnut Hills administration cancelled classes. Many of her friends that I interviewed did the same thing; parents went to work, while the children stayed closeted in their homes to avoid going anywhere near the riots. While many of those other children "goofed off," playing video games, practicing guitar riffs, chatting on their phones with friends, or just sleeping, Leah studiously worked on her senior paper and practiced piano. That is what Sarah Marcus reported as she checked in with Leah three times during the day to make sure her daughter was okay.

Chapter Eight

Last Day

I spent a lot of time with Sarah Marcus long after the spring of the riots. We spent many hours talking in her home and touring Walnut Hills High School together. I remember one interview when we sat in the theater, the magnificent home of the Arts Department, with masks of tragedy and comedy adorning the Rookwood Pottery proscenium arch above the stage. Sarah Marcus, even seventeen years after her daughter's death, wept at the memory of her sweet child, her most precious creation that would never learn the joy, or sorrow, of having children of her own.

Thursday, April 12, was Leah's last day of life. Because school was cancelled, she stayed home doing homework, working on her senior paper, and, of course, practicing piano. When Sarah Marcus allowed me access to the home on Burton Woods Lane, she gave me a tour of the house, including Leah's old bedroom. She left the room exactly as Leah had it furnished and decorated. Well, almost exactly. The bloodstains on the rug had been cleaned, and other items of disarray that she found upon discovering Leah's body had been taken care of. What struck me was the shrine-like atmosphere of the room of a child dead almost twenty years. Time had stopped; nothing would change in there as it never would for Leah Marcus after her death.

Sarah spent about ten minutes directing my attention to various items. I saw the prom dress that Leah had picked out for senior prom, but never got to wear. I saw the favored Winnie the Pooh teddy bear that Leah lugged around from the age of two until she was, Sarah recalled, laughing, almost thirteen. While Leah never played with Winnie any more, he had a seat of honor snuggled in a lounge chair in the corner of her room. I saw the trophies that Leah won at piano competitions, pictures of her with her friends adorning a corkboard over her bed. I saw her CD collection, hundreds of them, music of every conceivable genre. Flipping through the cases, I saw that her tastes went well beyond the Classical music she played on the piano. Among the possessions Sarah showed me was Leah's old cell phone, an obsolete Nokia flip phone that still lies on her dresser, plugged into a wall outlet for a charge, awaiting a call or text that will never come. The Marcuses cancelled the cell account from Cincinnati Bell for Leah's line not long after Leah's murder when the phone started receiving anonymous text messages. Despite their horror and grief, the Marcuses never erased those post-mortem messages, some of which she showed to me. "Slut," "whore," "you got what you deserved," and a whole litany of disgusting such items, gushed from the back-lit face of her phone, still capable of causing hurt years later as evidenced by the anguished look on Sarah Marcus's face.

On Thursday, both Ben and Sarah went to work. Ben worked at his downtown office. Despite the riots, it was relatively easy and safe to get to downtown. Ben actually double-backed north up Reading Road a couple of miles, got on the Norwood Lateral eastbound to I-71, which took him downtown in relative ease. His office on Fourth Street was blocks away from the rioting, the worst of which was occurring after nightfall, anyway. He made sure during the week of the riots to leave before sundown. Sarah worked north of town in a bedroom community known as Sharonville. It was due north of her home, right up Reading Road about six miles. The North Avondale house put Ben and Sarah practically equidistant to their respective offices; this was one of the prime determinants the family factored in when choosing a home.

Sarah told me that she spoke with Leah by telephone during her lunch hour that day. Everything was fine, Leah reported. The neighborhood was safe; she was working on her paper. She planned on practicing piano sometime after lunch. Sarah made Leah promise that she would stay inside and just make lunch in the kitchen. She "ordered" Leah not to leave the house. Leah promised she would do so. They never spoke again.

I sensed that Sarah was worried about Leah, even though the riots had come nowhere near North Avondale. Sarah left her office early, at 3:45, to go home. "Things were in order; it was a slow day, what with the riots going on." She drove the six miles south to her home. When she arrived, nothing seemed amiss. Leah's car was in the garage. All the doors to the house were locked. But when she shouted out to Leah that she was home, no response emanated from anywhere in the house. She called several more times, exploring the first floor looking for Leah.

Sarah entered the house from the rear entrance. The home is so old, there is no attached garage; the garage sits on the rear of the lot. When she walked into the foyer, she had the first indication that something was terribly wrong. On the landing before the staircase, there were bloodstains on the floor. As her eyes gazed upwards, she saw more blood on the stairs. She shouted Leah's name and sprinted up the stairs, two at a time, heading directly for Leah's room. She rushed to her daughter's room; the door was shut. She didn't bother knocking. The small drops of blood led directly from downstairs to this very door. She threw the door open and screamed at the sight.

Leah had a large upstairs bedroom. Large enough to comfortably hold a double bed, a dresser, two night tables, a desk and chair for homework, two wing chairs that sat before a fireplace, various bookshelves, and the chaise lounge that Winnie the Pooh called home. Oriental strip rugs ran the length of the bed, and at the foot of the bed, there was a five-by-seven-foot Oriental rug that faced the fireplace. On that rug, Sarah Marcus found her daughter, naked, hands bound behind her back, lying on her left side, a ligature wrapped around her neck. She couldn't see it well, but Leah was bleeding from a head wound to the left temple. Blood pooled on the rug. The bed was in disarray. Sarah sank to her knees, feeling for a pulse on her daughter's neck, putting her ear to her daughter's lips to hear the sound of breaths escaping, then to her chest to listen for perhaps the faint beat of her heart. It was clear to her that Leah was dead. Her eyes were open, petechiae burst over the sclera. She took two fingertips and closed the lids, to shut them out from having to relive a horror that seemed impossible to contemplate.

Sarah knew that Leah was dead. Sarah also knew that she had to call the police. She knew that various ignominies were soon to occur regarding Leah's dead body. But, in that moment, she could not bear to let her child's nakedness be the object of cynical and disrespectful, and God forbid, the impudent, jocular, derisive, and offensive comments that strangers long-accustomed to death, the police, the EMTs, the crime technicians, and the morgue personnel, would soon utter. Sarah pulled the comforter off of Leah's bed and covered her daughter's body up to the neck. Little did she know that that action would become one of the center points of Damon Allbright's defense case.

Chapter Nine

First Response

Sarah Marcus called 9-1-1 at 4:10 p.m. that afternoon. Unlike a lot of 9-1-1 audios you may have heard over the years, Sarah's voice does not rise in pitch and tempo; there is no fear or anxiousness in her voice. She sounds calm, cool, dispassionate. Shocked or disassociated might be more accurate.

"Nine one one. What is your emergency?"

"This is Sarah Marcus. I live at Nine Burton Woods Lane in North Avondale."

"Yes, ma'am."

"I just arrived home from work. My daughter, Leah. She's dead in the house. She has been murdered."

"Are you sure she's dead?"

"I checked for a pulse. Breathing. Nothing. She's bleeding from a head wound. There's a cord tied around her neck. Her eyes were open. Staring."

"I'll send EMT just in case, along with the police. Is the perpetrator in the house? Are you safe?"

"I'm safe. There's no one else in the home."

"Yes, ma'am. Dispatching now."

The 9-1-1 operator relayed the message to the District Four police station about a mile north of the Marcus home on Reading Road. She also notified the Fire Division, District Three in that case, Company 32, just south of the Marcus house on Forest Avenue, just off of Reading Road.

The first responder was a District Four police officer, Miranda Noble, who was in her cruiser less than half a mile away when the call came through. She flipped on her lights and siren and, within a minute, pulled in front of the Marcus home. Sarah Marcus heard the siren and left Leah's room to open the door to the officer.

Noble, who I interviewed, was no longer a rookie in 2001, but then was only two years on the job. She had only seen a handful of bodies at that point in her career, all young, African American men shot dead in apparent drug turf-war disputes. She had seen men shot in the head, hit six times in the torso and head, and even in the groin and buttocks. But she had never before seen a beautiful, young teenage girl killed, and probably raped, though she didn't mention that to Sarah.

She had Sarah Marcus show her the body. Miranda checked for signs of life and called it in to dispatch that the girl was, in fact, deceased, and that detectives, the coroner, and crime scene technicians would be needed. She took Sarah Marcus out of the bedroom and back downstairs to the front parlor, door locked in case the perpetrator was still in the house, to await the next arrivals. After searching the house to make sure the perpetrator still wasn't there, she returned to Sarah in the parlor. By that time,

Company 32 of the Fire Division had arrived, an EMT truck as well as a fire truck. Noble let them in, and they proceeded upstairs to examine the body, and again, to corroborate what Sarah Marcus already knew, that her daughter was, indeed, dead.

Years later, Noble still recalls this case, the first homicide to haunt her dreams. She remembers Sarah Marcus finally breaking down and crying in the parlor. She remembers offering her condolences, trying to remain the professional police officer, but in light of the woman sobbing in front of her, finally, taking Mrs. Marcus in her arms, hugging her, and rubbing her back.

While Noble was upstairs with the Company 32 responders, Sarah took a minute to call her husband, Ben, at the office. She recalls that Ben's secretary told her that he was in the middle of a deposition, and could she take a message and have him call her back? Sarah responded, no she could not wait, not a single minute, not a second; this was an emergency, and she needed to interrupt the proceedings.

In one of those "I can't believe it" moments that happens to most of us, Sarah recalls Ben being rather abrupt with her for interrupting his deposition. "What is so important to interrupt the Weatherby case?" Ben apparently wasn't thinking of Sarah, Leah, the riots, or anything but the matter at hand. It's not that he was an inattentive husband or father, merely that, like a lot of workaholics, he was task-oriented.

"Ben," Sarah told her husband. "It's Leah," she said.

"What about Leah?"

"She's dead."

Sarah can't recall how long the silence lasted on the phone. It seemed to her an eternity. The amount of time it took Ben's usually nimble brain to process her statement failed him at an inopportune time.

"What?"

"I found her at home. After work. Someone killed her."

After relaying the basic facts, Ben told her that he would be right home. By the time he was able to extricate himself from the deposition, his office, and his parking garage, navigate downtown traffic, and take a chance driving his black Mercedes with the vanity plate "CR 23"[2] through the vestiges of the riots straight up Reading Road from downtown, forty-five minutes had elapsed before he arrived at Burton Woods Lane.

When he turned onto his street, which was just a quick jaunt off of northbound Reading Road to Clinton Springs and then three streets on the right, he found that he couldn't get anywhere near his house. On both sides of the street and even in his driveway, he found police cars, fire trucks, EMT vans with lights flashing. There were other obvious official vehicles, Crown Vic sedans with city plates, that parked on both sides of the

---

[2] Federal Civil Rule 23 covers class action lawsuits. Ben Marcus utilized that rule in multiple lawsuits that he filed over his career.

street for dozens of yards in either direction. He parked a quarter-mile up the street and walked back to his house. Neighbors and passers-by started to congregate around the Marcus home, held back by a cordon of officials. A patrol officer intercepted Ben but finally let him under the crime scene tape when he showed his identification.

He found Sarah downstairs, still accompanied by Miranda Noble, her unofficial *chargé-d'affaires*, and they hugged. Sarah was no longer crying, but her eyes glistened red-rimmed, and her mascara streaked down her face. He told her he was going upstairs to look at Leah's body. At the top of the stairwell, another patrol officer stopped him, but Ben insisted on proceeding. The officer spoke into his radio, and half a minute later, a police detective exited Leah's room and introduced himself to Ben Marcus.

His name was Simon Bergdorf. Ben Marcus recalls meeting a slight, almost diminutive man in a rumpled suit with glasses, who looked more like a mathematics professor than a homicide detective. Bergdorf is one of those people you meet that you just cannot believe they are as good as their reputation suggests. Like all the other homicide detectives, he had come up from the world of street cops. He worked District Four for five years before joining that district's squad of detectives. After a few years on that job, the lieutenant in charge of the Homicide Squad, who had been following Bergdorf's career, invited the young detective to join Homicide. By the time he was only thirty-five, Bergdorf morphed from street cop to homicide detective. Bergdorf was intimately familiar with the Marcuses' neighborhood, having driven those streets for years in his patrol car, daydreaming what it must be like to have money and live in such fancy and fashionable houses, with manicured lawns and actual lawn service people to cut the grass, mulch the beds, and weed the gardens. In 2001, he was a forty-three-year-old man who had been investigating murders for seven years. He had closed over eighty percent of his cases.[3] He doesn't have the

---

[3] The national average for homicide clearances in 2001 was sixty-five percent according to the FBI. However, there is considerable debate over what a "cleared" homicide means. To some researchers, the definition is: "[A]n offense is said to be cleared up if a person has been charged, summonsed or cautioned for the offense, if the offense is admitted and taken into consideration by the court, or if there is sufficient evidence to charge a person, but the case is not proceeded with..." Other researchers define a cleared case as, "[W]hen police have identified a perpetrator, have sufficient evidence to charge him, and actually take him into custody," or he dies or is already in custody. Homicide clearance rates used to be ninety-three percent thirty years before Leah's death because most homicides were committed by persons who knew the victims. With the proliferation of drugs and guns, stranger-to-stranger homicides are becoming more prevalent, and these cases are harder to clear.

macho swagger of a homicide detective nor the big, weight-lifting toned body of many street cops. But he is smart, thorough, unrelenting, and his mild manners belie the fire that burns within. He is adept at interviewing suspects and getting them to confess. In foul weather, he wears a trench coat, and his colleagues nicknamed him "Columbo" after the frumpled TV detective portrayed by the late actor, Peter Falk.

"Mr. Marcus," Bergdorf began his apology, "my condolences. We have an active crime scene down the hall, and it would be inappropriate to let you in there. Besides, I don't think you want to see your daughter like that." Ben Marcus still recalls those words. He advised Bergdorf that he is a lawyer, a former prosecutor, and a father. He insisted. Bergdorf compromised by letting Marcus walk down the hallway, peer into the room, without actually entering it or touching anything, least of all Leah's body, and then escorting him back to the stairway. They spoke for a few minutes before Bergdorf excused himself to get back to work.

Ben still recalls the sight of Leah's body, still covered by the comforter Sarah laid over the body. Her bare feet protruded out from under the cover, and he could see the cord knotted around his daughter's neck, so tightly that the skin was compressed. As an elite litigator, Ben Marcus knew how to shepherd a case through the court system. He would utilize those skills to hound the investigators working Leah's murder. Within a week, he took a leave of absence from his firm (he owned it after all; who would complain?) to monitor and assist the police in any way he could.

Among those observing the early proceedings of the case was Vernon Banks, the creepy neighbor who lived in his parents' house in a third-floor attic converted into a bedroom suite, three doors down the street. Vernon didn't work; he was a felon with an extensive criminal record and, like many felons, found it difficult to find employment after his time in the penitentiary. Banks occupied his time in several ways, including listening to his police radio scanner. He also liked to watch porn on his computer up in the attic, including sick varieties of torture porn.

Eventually, Detective Bergdorf would come knocking on Vernon Banks's door. Leah's death occurred more than two years before Ohio enacted a registered sex offender law. But the thorough detective would soon learn that Banks was a sex offender. He had done multiple stints in prison for assaulting teenage girls.

Chapter Ten

Crime Scene

Detective Bergdorf waited for someone from the coroner's office to arrive to start work, as well has his own office's criminalists who would collect evidence. He also waited for his partner, Detective Rita Nowakowski, to show up. They usually travelled together, but she had taken a few hours off for a doctor's appointment. She got the call and drove separately. The coroner's van arrived ten minutes after Rita. He filled her in on the fly as they walked upstairs. He had already done some preliminary work at the scene. Crime scene photographers snapped scores of pictures. Other technicians lifted fingerprints off of various objects in the room, swept the rugs, floors, and the bedsheets with a vacuum to collect trace evidence.

When Bergdorf arrived on scene, his eye focused on the center of attention, the young woman dead on the rug at the foot of her bed, practically in the center of the room. But his practiced eye took in a wealth of other details. The bed was in disarray. The comforter, probably from the bed (he would check with the Marcuses), covered Leah's body. The bedsheets were pulled back and "mussed" as was a light spring-weight cotton blanket. Various belts, no doubt from Leah's closet, hung from the four posts of the bed; two dangled to the floor at the foot of the bed, and two were draped across the bed itself. The bedsheets soaked with blood. When he peeled back the blanket later, he saw ligature marks on Leah's wrists, which were still bound by yet a fifth belt, but also around her ankles. He surmised that she had been sexually assaulted, but wondered if her hands were tied behind her back, why were there two additional restraining articles at the head of her bed? Why would the perpetrator need them to restrain her upper extremities if her arms were already tied behind her back? Or did he rape her first, spread-eagled, then tie her hands behind her back when he was finished?

Her skin was still warm to the touch, so she had been dead for a relatively short period of time; body temperature, he knew, cools off at between one and two degrees per hour depending on the ambient temperature of the environment. A formidable pool of blood soaked the carpet at the left side of her head. She lay on her left side with no obvious lividity occurring yet, which was expected given the probable recent death. Her skin still blanched when he pushed on the skin of her calf. There were petechiae in both eyes, so despite the head wound, she had probably been asphyxiated with the cord tied around her neck. The head wound most likely came from a bronze statue, which he found bloodstained and lying on another Oriental rug in the entrance hall. Sarah told him that the statue was a piece of art she had collected on a trip to Greece and the sole adornment of a credenza in the foyer.

Miranda Noble already told him that Sarah Marcus had not noted any signs of forced entry, nor had Noble on her walkabout of the perimeter. Bergdorf toured the house top to bottom just to satisfy himself that was the case. Given no signs of forced entry, and Sarah Marcus having assured him that Leah would never stay at home with the door unlocked, and certainly not during the pendency of the riots, Bergdorf concluded that Leah had let her assailant into the house voluntarily. She probably, although not necessarily, knew the person. Leah and her assailant spoke in the foyer. They may or may not have left the foyer before the attacker bludgeoned Leah. But at some point, even if they had left the entrance hall, they returned to that room. There, the assailant, who probably was right-handed given the blow to Leah's left temple, picked up the statue, which weighed over ten pounds, and whacked her sufficiently hard to make Leah fall to the floor. A substantial amount of blood soaked into the entrance hall rug. Whether Leah suffered a skull fracture would be determined at the autopsy. But certainly, the blow was forceful enough to knock her to the floor. The assailant then carried, or dragged, Leah up the stairs to the bedroom. It is doubtful that she walked voluntarily up the staircase given how much blood Bergdorf found in the foyer. Combined with the amount of blood in the upstairs bedroom, Leah sustained a serious wound, but not necessarily enough to kill her. At any given time, a fifth to a quarter of a person's blood is circulating through the head, evidence of the enormous need for oxygen and glucose by the brain. Even a small cut to the scalp can bleed copiously, he knew.

Like Bergdorf, Nowakowski relished in the role of homicide detective. Nowakowski had worked with Bergdorf for over a year. They were partners, at Bergdorf's request, she gleaned; although, the Homicide commander told her it was his decision. When I spoke with Rita in researching this book, I saw a fiftyish woman, still very attractive, who had risen to be lieutenant in charge of the Homicide bureau. She showed me her Academy graduation picture, a twenty-three-year-old woman with black hair and dark eyes gleaming, very official-looking but also very beautiful. Coming up as a patrol officer, even in the 1990s, Rita Nowakowski had to deal with a lot of gender bias in a profession that historically was male-dominated. Being a woman was tough; being a beautiful woman meant colleagues took her even less seriously. Some of the older officers, who grew up during the 1960s, called her "Lovely Rita" or "Meter Maid" in reference to the old Beatles song. The Meter Maid title was doubly offensive to Nowakowski because she was a patrol officer, not a meter maid. They were deliberately demeaning her status. And if she rose to the bait of their taunts, then she was a poor sport and a shrew; and if she let it slide, she was just "Lovely Rita," a token woman on the force. She never felt that way around Bergdorf, a, by all accounts, happily married man with school-age children. She sensed that he wanted to be around her because of her intellect. Together, she and Bergdorf made quite a team and cleared more cases on a percentage basis than any other team of detectives on the squad.

Rita learned from Simon, soaked up his expertise and his knowledge, and knew she had the best mentor on the force. He respected her as a detective because she was smart, not because she was a woman detective, and so the eye candy was just a gratuitous added bonus. She started to think like Bergdorf. Looking at the statue on the rug, she told him, "She didn't necessarily know the perp. It could have been a delivery guy with a line about a box or someone looking for directions. Someone non-threatening."

"It could have been anyone. Even Ben Marcus. No one is ruled out yet."

"I doubt he killed and sexually assaulted his own daughter."

"We don't know that she was sexually assaulted. But until we verify that he was at work, even he's on the list."

Rita knew that Simon was gently reminding her that anything was possible this early on in an investigation. There could be no "rush to judgment." Like Bergdorf, Nowakowski was well-acquainted with the statistic that most murders are committed by someone who knows the victim.

Simon also apparently sensed that this case was going to be high profile given the victim, her family, and the neighborhood. "We have to do this case right," he told her.

"After we're through here, I'll organize people to canvass the neighborhood," she offered.

"Thanks. Have someone start taking a census of security cameras around the neighborhood. I doubt there are any on this street, but you never know. Someone might be a little paranoid about security. There will be some in the businesses nearby. We might get a car or a person to track down."

While they discussed early-stage strategy, the coroner's van finally arrived. The deputy coroner who exited was Allison Pollard, a forty-five-year-old pathologist who had been with the coroner's office since completing her residency and fellowships after graduating from medical school. She liked to not only do the autopsy, but to be at the crime scene as well. She thought the crime scene told a story, a story which, if she only looked at photographs after the fact, meant that she had only a tenth of the data available to her. She knew Bergdorf quite well and was getting fast acquainted with Nowakowski now that she and Simon were partners.

Bergdorf gave her the quick rundown, showed her the foyer, the blood trail leading up to Leah's bedroom, and, finally, the crime scene itself. Pollard told me later, when I interviewed her, that the first thing she noticed upon entering the room, like Bergdorf, was Leah's body on the floor. As she crouched down for a closer look, the most memorable sensations were of smell; the smell of spilt blood and urine assailed her nostrils. She knew that people can voluntarily block four of their five senses—touch, hearing, taste, and sight. But humans have no capacity to block the sense of smell. Assuming the mechanism of the nose is intact along with Cranial Nerve I, which transmits smells to the brain as an electrical impulse, a person will never be able to ignore smell. This, she assumed, was an evolutionary holdover from a time when smelling a predator coming after you was often the first notice you had that you might become some animal's dinner. After death, a person's urinary and anal sphincters relax, allowing the contents of the bladder and bowels to leak out; hence, the smell of urine. What she didn't smell or see were feces. Apparently, Leah had voluntarily evacuated her bowels not too long before she was killed. Perhaps she had eaten since then; this would be determined upon autopsy. But if she had, the contents of her meal most likely remained in her stomach. The digestive process had not moved them along to her bowels yet.

Pollard went to work. She removed the comforter from Leah's body and examined her in place. She touched various parts of Leah's body, feeling for warmth and lividity. She looked closely at the head wound, the cord around the neck, the ligature marks around all four extremities. She took a thermometer and obtained a rectal temperature. "Ninety-five degrees," she announced. She knew enough that that put Leah's death within the last few hours, but ascribing an actual time of death, in the absence of a witness, was something that coroners cannot do with absolute specificity. "It also appears she was sexually assaulted. There's

79

bruising around the anus and labia," she announced. Back at the morgue, she would swab Leah's body, looking for semen that she could analyze. A wealth of evidence about a perpetrator could be established with semen. DNA would pinpoint a perpetrator to within greater than a one-in-a-quadrillion chance. Properly handled and presented in court, such evidence could be devastating to a defendant who claimed, "It wasn't me!" Pollard also told me when I interviewed her that DNA evidence could exonerate convicted prisoners, and she had made that clear in publications she authored before the spate of conviction reversals premised on DNA evidence became commonplace.

She pressed lightly on the head wound, trying to feel for any obvious deformities, indentations, or movement that would suggest a skull fracture, but she didn't find any. "My sense is that she died by asphyxiation not by blunt force trauma to the head," she said, echoing Bergdorf's assessment. "But we will know more after the post-mortem." She wanted to know if the victim's body was found like this *in situ.* Bergdorf confirmed that, not yet having spoken to Sarah Marcus about the fact that she covered the body with the comforter from the bed. Looking around the room, she noticed a floor lamp toppled over near the fireplace. The power cord was missing. Looking at Leah's neck, she realized that the perpetrator had ripped the cord out of the lamp and used it as the tool to strangle Leah. She looked at Leah's hands closely and noticed specks of blood under the nails of her right hand. She would scrape those nails later, looking for DNA. Leah may have fought back and been able to scratch her attacker. DNA from multiple sources might confirm the attacker's identity and even indicate if there were more than one perpetrator. She "bagged" Leah's hands to preserve any DNA evidence under the nails.

"I'll need those belts," she said, pointing to the ones tied to the bedposts, "to compare them to the bruises on her wrists and ankles. Just to make sure that those are the instruments that she was tied with. There also might be DNA other than Leah's on them." Bergdorf assured her they would go with the coroner's people back to the coroner's office. "I will need all the bed coverings as well. Check them for semen, pubic hair, any evidence that we can trace back to the perpetrator. The statue down in the hall, too. To compare to her head wound." The coroner collected evidence from the body; the police collected evidence from the crime scene.

Pollard stood up, rising to her full five-foot-eleven height. She played volleyball as an undergrad at Temple University. She towered over Simon Bergdorf. "This is not our usual crime scene, is this, Simon?" she asked him. He shook his head in agreement. "You know who her father is?" she asked.

"I know he's a lawyer."

"He is." Pollard's husband was also a lawyer, and so she knew Ben Marcus's reputation. "He's one of the most famous trial attorneys in America. Very sharp. Watch yourself. I guarantee you he'll be watching you."

"Don't worry. We're going to catch this guy." Bergdorf wasn't worried about Ben Marcus. His only concern was bringing the perp to justice. It was the least he could do for Leah Marcus.

Chapter Eleven

Initial Interviews

Bergdorf and Nowakowski led the Marcuses to the family room at the back of the house to interview them. Partly, this gesture intended to put them at ease in a comfortable, less formal room of the house. Partly, it's meant to shield them from the sight of the coroner's people wheeling Leah's body away on a gurney to the van waiting outside in the driveway. A perimeter around the house kept neighbors, gawkers, and the first reporters away from the scene.

I interviewed Bergdorf ten years after Leah's death. We sat in his home office, with my recorder perched on the corner of his desk. We kept the door shut, so that his children, who were home for the summer, might not eavesdrop. His memory remained remarkably intact, aided by the triple reminders of one of his more unusual cases, his homicide case book, and the personal notes he wrote on index cards. The cards he carried around in his suit coat pocket, always available. Dated and numbered, they constituted an unofficial murder book. He would transfer relevant notes into the case file, but the index cards remained his personal property. He kept them in a banker's box in his home office, which he would sometimes refer to during the course of our more than ten hours of interviews over the course of a week in 2011.

Bergdorf opened his interview of the parents similar to his usual close family interviews. He offered his condolences. He assured the Marcuses that he personally, those who worked for him, and the entire Cincinnati Police Department would do their utmost to quickly identify Leah's killer. Or killers. Rather than just plow into the details he knew he had to inquire about, he asked the Marcuses to tell him and Rita about Leah. The purpose of this question was twofold. First and foremost, it put the parents at ease. Second, parents' discussion of their child often yielded clues as to who might be responsible. After the Marcuses spent fifteen minutes describing Leah, Simon Bergdorf felt a little, in his words, "like the air had been let out of my balloon. This was such a wonderful young person on the verge of adulthood. The world lost a treasure. She would have been a pediatric neurosurgeon, saving the lives of other parents' children with brain tumors. She might still have pursued her interest in music, perhaps becoming a YouTube sensation. Who knows. What was apparent was that she was a sweet soul, with no apparent enemies. I was leaning to a stranger attacking her; that in her naiveté, she let someone into the house in an effort to help and that led to her demise. Then Sarah told me about Leah's breakup with Damon Allbright five days before, on Saturday night."

Bergdorf had asked the parents if they had any idea, any idea at all, who might have wanted to hurt Leah. Sarah and Ben exchanged one of those "knowing, silent glances," (Bergdorf's words) before Ben finally nodded. Sarah then told him that Leah broke up with her boyfriend the previous Saturday night. Sarah explained why Leah told her she had broken up. Leah was not exactly devastated, but she was very sad. Bergdorf asked who the boyfriend was. When Sarah said the name, Bergdorf was thinking to himself, he told me, "Is that Othello Allbright's son?" Simon was no stranger to the riots and the events that precipitated them. He knew that Othello Allbright served as the tip of the spear, the thorn in city hall's side on Monday during the council meeting. When Sarah confirmed that Damon was Othello's son, the next thought that crossed Simon's mind was, "Oh shit. This just got much more complicated. And political." Not that, he assured me, that would make a whit of difference with how he would prosecute the investigation. His job was to identify the perp; others could be the lawyers, the prosecutors, the judge, and the spin doctors.

Rita wanted to know if the Marcuses knew whether there was any history of violence or even controlling behavior by Damon toward Leah. They assured her that as far as they knew, there was no such history. In their estimation, Damon was a thoughtful and respectful young man, a good boyfriend to their daughter. Sarah's willingness to put Damon's name before the investigators, then claim he was such a nice young man rang slightly hollow with Bergdorf, but he couldn't quite put his finger on why Sarah Marcus might act that way. Perhaps it simply meant the stress of the murder had changed the clarity of her observations. He knew from talking to the parents that both Ben and Sarah Marcus occupied alpha roles in the community, just as the Reverend Allbright did. She wasn't saying that Damon did it exactly. Sarah opined that she thought the killer must be somehow related to the riots. Her insight, it would ultimately prove, was prescient.

At that point in the interview, Simon got up from behind the desk in his home office and walked over to a wall of bookcases that lined the length of the room. He explained that he liked Greek history and literature, and pulled a copy of *The Iliad* off one of the shelves. "It must be what the gods on Olympus felt when they mucked around with the lives of the kings and queens of Troy and Greece. Let's get the best of humanity, rip the guts out of them, and see how it all shakes out. And it was happening again, right here in North Avondale." Until that point, I didn't know Bergdorf knew much about history or literature. But his was not the only comment about tragedy, in the Classical Greek sense, that I heard while doing interviews for this book.

Bergdorf then asked the Marcuses for their own timeline of events, which he would verify later with their colleagues. Not that he suspected the parents of filicide, but that he had to rule everyone out as a possible suspect. He then asked them to pack some bags and prepare to spend some time away from home. The investigators would spend the next day, at least, gathering forensic details. Besides, he told them, it would be just too heartbreaking to stay there that night.

Before Simon and Rita interviewed the parents, Rita organized a small battalion of patrol officers to canvass the neighborhood. The first interesting development came about 7:00 p.m. that evening when an officer interviewed Alice Bowman, the eighty-year-old widow who lived four doors down the street from the Marcuses, right next door to Vernon Banks. The officer contacted Bergdorf, and after he and Nowakowski finished with the Marcuses, they walked down the tree-lined street. They spent several hours at 9 Burton Woods Lane, while the sun sank lower on the horizon. By the time they finished for the evening, it was almost nine. The sun set at 8:12 p.m. They walked down the gaslight lit street to Alice Bowman's house. The officer waited for them on the front porch. After a quick rundown, they rang the bell, and Alice answered the door not ten seconds later. For a spry eighty-year-old, she must nevertheless have been waiting in the front room. She asked them in, offered them coffee or tea, which they refused, and then told them her story. Her husband had passed away more than a year ago. She had been considering selling the house, but she was still in good shape and didn't mind the stairs. She loved the old house and walking in the neighborhood. But with her husband gone, she found she often sat on the front verandah, reading a book, and sipping from a pitcher of iced tea. She didn't mind the cooler weather, but the spring had been unusually warm. That day, the high hit eighty-six degrees, so the iced tea actually kept her cool despite the heat. Her covered porch helped, too, she added. While reading her book, *The World According to Garp*, she made note to tell the detectives, she heard the sound of a car coming down the street. This was at 1:48, she recalled, because she checked her wristwatch. It was unusual to see cars, or people, for that matter, in the neighborhood at that time of day. Most folks had already left for school and work, and nobody would be coming home for a least an hour (the schoolkids) and even later for the men and women who worked.

Bergdorf inquired what else captured her attention about this vehicle. Alice explained that the driver came in pretty fast, "at least ten miles an hour over the speed limit, maybe more," and stopped one door further down the street from her, making the car's destination even further from the Marcus home. Yet, the woman who got out of the car walked back in the direction of the Marcus house as if she knew exactly where it was. It was odd to Alice because she figured if you didn't know where the Marcus home was, you would have been driving very slowly looking for the address. But if you already knew where the house was, why would you park five houses down the street and then walk back to it?

Alice Bowman couldn't describe the woman very well. She parked on the other side of the street and was a fair distance from Alice's verandah. She also was wearing her reading glasses to see her book. Her regular glasses, which she usually wore on a chain around her neck, she inadvertently left in the house. She couldn't give a very good description to the detectives. The woman was blonde, or at least light brown haired, between twenty and forty years old, not fat, not thin. She wore jeans and a dark top, sunglasses, a baseball cap with a ponytail sticking out the back. The car, well, Alice couldn't tell a Studebaker from a Ford. It was a sedan, or maybe a coupé, black or dark blue. License plate? The detectives were joking when they asked her if she could read that, right, she asked.

Rita peered down the street from the verandah when they finished the interview. Given the arc of the street, you couldn't actually see the Marcus house from Bowman's front porch. At best, it was very circumstantial evidence that this mystery woman even went to 9 Burton Woods Lane at all.

It wasn't much to go on at all, although, it would be duly noted in Bergdorf's official file as well as his index cards. But Damon Allbright's lawyer would do his best to get his client off based on this witness.

Chapter Twelve

Friday, April 13

Simon Bergdorf and Rita Nowakowski finally made it back to the Homicide bureau around 10:30 p.m. They wrote their reports, said goodnight, and returned to their homes. Simon alerted his wife that he was going to be late; she was still up when he got back home just after midnight. He rarely talked cases with his wife. It was hard to be a cop's spouse if you weren't one yourself. Especially for street officers, the risk of getting injured or killed on the job put the most stalwart spouses on edge. As a detective, his personal risk was reduced, but the emotional toll it took on him strained him and his wife. She didn't pester him about cases unless he wanted to talk.

He wanted to talk about the Leah Marcus case. He poured his heart out to her that night, and would do so several more times during the course of the investigation and trial. On little sleep, he returned to the office at 0800 hours the next morning and filled in his supervisor, Lieutenant Daniel Horstmeyer. By the time I interviewed Bergdorf for this book, Horstmeyer had passed away, prematurely of a heart attack at age fifty-seven in 2007. Bergdorf had a low opinion of Horstmeyer, and his willingness to

talk demonstrated his knowledge of libel law—
that one cannot slander the dead. At least not
legally. Horstmeyer was a "pol" in Bergdorf's
opinion. A politician first and a cop second. His
interest always was what was best for
Horstmeyer, not what was best for the case, the
department, or the city. Horstmeyer thought he
was going to be chief some day and that was
what mattered most to him, in Bergdorf's
opinion. Simon and Rita gave the lieutenant their
initial rundown.

     "Jesus," Horstmeyer burst forth upon
hearing that a person of interest was Damon
Allbright, not noticing the irony of his
exclamation in that Damon was the son of a
minister. "Allbright? The son of the guy who held
up city hall?" That metaphor, however, was an
apt one, as the Reverend Allbright had all but
held up the council chambers four long days
before. "Before you pin it on the kid, make sure
he did it," Horstmeyer admonished his
detectives. "The blacks don't need something
else to get riled up about." The term "the blacks"
was Horstmeyer's code word for the "N" word.
Simon never heard Horstmeyer utter the term
"African American" except at a press conference.
In private, he was an unabashed racist. The
community of African Americans had long
charged the CPD with being racist; Bergdorf
sometimes privately acknowledged that the
moniker was fairly earned. Nor was it just the
community that charged the department with
racism. Black officers, represented by the
Sentinel Police Association, levelled the same
charge.

Bergdorf returned to his desk for a moment to clarify his thoughts on the next step in the investigation. That was when his telephone rang. I was the caller that morning, having started to work the case the day before for the *Tribune*. I wanted a statement from Simon, or at least some off-the-record background information, that I could use for the afternoon edition.

I still have my notes from my early days as the crime reporter. These are spiral-bound notepads categorized by date. In scribbled handwriting, decipherable by none but myself, I wrote that Bergdorf was not willing at that time to go on the record. He indicated death appeared to be by strangulation, but the official cause of death would have to await the autopsy report, which could take up to a few weeks. She had been found naked and bound, with evidence of sexual assault. But I had circled the comment on my notepad and wrote, "Doesn't that suggest rape?" Not necessarily, the investigator responded; it could have been rough sex that got out of control. No suspects had been identified. There was no evidence of a break-in. Didn't that suggest, I wrote as a question, that Leah knew her assailant and let him in? Not necessarily, the detective responded again.

My notes were bland and basically drivel; the sort of thing that gets published in the newspaper while quoting "unnamed sources within the police department." Something to put in the paper to let the public know we were working the case. Something to let the guys at the *Enquirer*, the other hometown newspaper, know that we didn't intend to take a back seat to them on this case. Even that early on, I sensed a high-profile case with a young, attractive murder victim from an affluent neighborhood. (I had already found a copy of the year 2000 *Remembrancer*, the Walnut Hills high school yearbook, where I saw my first picture of Leah Marcus.)

Bergdorf and Nowakowski knew that Walnut Hills was still closed for the riots, so they intended to get right at it with an interview of Damon Allbright. Pollard told them she would do the autopsy in the afternoon, and they assured her they would be back at the morgue in time for the proceedings.

The Allbrights lived at an impressive home at 937 Redway Avenue across Reading Road from the Marcuses' neighborhood. The Redway home was a massive Italianate home built in 1908 with thirteen rooms and five bedrooms sitting on almost a half-acre of land. The Allbrights needed those five bedrooms as they had six children. Growing up, some of the children had to share a bedroom even with that plethora of sleeping rooms in the home. Damon was third-born of those six children; the older two had already left the house to attend college, or in the eldest's case, Mary, to work as a lawyer in Columbus where she had been hired after clerking at a law firm there while still attending Ohio State University.

The detectives drove up Reading Road from their downtown office to North Avondale and parked on the street. They walked up the slight rise to the home, passing planters filled with spring flowers of various colors in full bloom due to the unusually recent warm weather. They passed well-tended, landscaped areas, along with a lawn, Simon noted, that had been edged along the sidewalks and driveway. They rang the doorbell, and soon, the door opened, held by the youngest Allbright child, Marcus, a thin boy of ten who politely inquired who they were and what they wanted. They introduced themselves, and he said he would call his mother; would they please wait outside until she returned? He was not allowed to let strangers enter the house without her permission.

Delores Allbright returned in a minute and asked the detectives to enter. At the time, she was forty-eight, tall, flowing hair turning to gray, and held herself erect, ramrod straight. She asked them into the front sitting room and inquired to the nature of their visit. Bergdorf asked if Damon was home, and Delores said yes, school was cancelled; he was in his room. They asked her to ask him to join them, and she left, a quizzical look on her face. Damon joined the group in a relaxed state, Bergdorf noted. He wore sweatpants and a Walnut Hills sweatshirt but not a hoodie. He later learned that the Allbrights discouraged their boys from wearing hoodies due to the undesirable impression they gave of young black men being criminals.

Damon was a handsome young man, six feet tall, 175 pounds of lean muscle, skin the color of dark caramel, who carried his body with the easy grace of the athlete that he was. Nowakowski told me when I interviewed her years later that she could definitely see the girls' heads at the school turn when Damon walked by.

Bergdorf introduced himself and his partner to Damon and asked if Damon would come downtown with them to talk about a case. The detectives preferred to interview witnesses/suspects on their home turf. Delores said Damon was not going anywhere until they told her more about what they wanted to talk to him about. Simon asked Damon if he knew why the detectives were there that morning.

"No, sir," Damon answered, demonstrating the politeness and respect for authority with which he was raised.

"Leah Marcus is dead, Damon," Bergdorf told him. Bergdorf still recalls Damon's expression. "We wanted to know if you could help us find out what happened to your girlfriend."

The young man couldn't even answer for a minute as a flash of shock washed over his face. Finally, he muttered, "What?"

In that moment Bergdorf, who owned an unofficial master's degree in reading people, believed that Damon had no idea that Leah was dead and, therefore, had nothing to do with her murder. Weeks later, when the DNA evidence came back, he would look back at that interview and conclude Damon was the consummate actor, perhaps a sociopath. A thought nagged at the corner of his mind, but he refused to say it to himself. He needn't have worried about articulating the thought. Lieutenant Horstmeyer would, Simon told me, be much less generous in his appraisal and more willing to express cruel opinions. Horstmeyer told the detective, "He's just a younger version of O. J. Simpson."

Chapter Thirteen

Two Denials

"Damon," Bergdorf asked, "I have to ask you a couple of questions." The young man stared back at the detective without responding. "School wasn't in session yesterday. Where were you yesterday afternoon?"

Still no response. In one of those eerie moments that most everyone has had on occasion, Bergdorf felt as if things moved in slow motion. He noted with precision his surroundings in the Allbright study. African masks adorned the walls. Wooden and stone carvings of elephants, giraffes, rhinoceroses, zebras, and antelopes from sub-Saharan Africa sat in mute silence on bookshelves, desks, and tables. He could feel the cool air from the paddle ceiling fan blow over his hair, and he could count the revolutions of the blades easily as they twirled around the center mast. He could hear with preternatural ability sounds throughout the house, the laundry machine running in the basement, the blower motor on the HVAC kicking off, a fly buzzing around the room. Bergdorf told me that he wanted to believe Damon was innocent, that he expected Damon to blurt out something obvious and verifiable without hesitation. Perhaps that he had a late lunch with his mother at a restaurant where there would be servers and hostesses and dishwashers who could serve as alibis for his whereabouts, while someone else was busy assaulting, raping, and killing Leah.

Instead, what he saw Damon do was, just for an instant, glance over at his mother and then look back at his interrogator. Bergdorf would never testify in court that such furtiveness equated with guilt. But he was good at reading body language, and he knew the averted eye signified deception. The detective was conflicted; the teenager sounded surprised at the announcement of Leah's death, yet he wouldn't be forthright and state where he was at the previous afternoon.

Delores Allbright also picked up on Damon's glance; their eyes locked for a moment. Bergdorf could tell, because before he could ask another question, she interjected. The rapidity with which her mind processed information was stunning. "What exactly happened to Leah, Detective?" she inquired.

"She was murdered," he responded. "In the bedroom of her home." The mouths of both Damon and his mother opened in "O" expressions of shock. Again, Simon felt that this was indeed news to Damon. No one can act that credibly and yet be lying.

"How?" Delores asked.

"We don't know for sure yet. We think she was strangled."

"Why?" Damon howled in anguish. This time the detectives, who went over the conversation after the fact, had no doubt that Damon told the truth; he had no idea Leah was dead. "Who would want to hurt her?" he continued. He put his head in his hands and sobbed. His mother put her arm on his shoulder. "I haven't seen her since Saturday night when we went out on a date."

"Why exactly do you want to know where Damon was yesterday?" Delores asked, her voice, tone, and pitch rising.

Simon could understand that she was the wife of a preacher. She was rising to oratory, and Simon realized he was going to get blasted by her words.

"Are you accusing my son of *murdering* Leah?" She let the words hang in the air, but not long enough for Bergdorf to get off a response. "He loved that girl."

"Mrs. Allbright—"

"Don't you 'Mrs. Allbright' me," Delores said, jabbing her index finger at him and striking out with fury in her voice. "You come into *my* house accusing *my* son of killing someone? He is a man of *peace*. A man of *God*. How dare you," she spat out each word, enunciating them with precision and emphasis.

Bergdorf knew from that moment that the race card would be played in this investigation. Delores Allbright was calling out the CPD for all the prior injustices it had suffered upon the African American community. He knew that her community would never give him, a white police detective, the benefit of the doubt nor anything more than the stoic courtesy of the oppressed in the face of caustic racism.

"Mrs. Allbright, please," Simon said, almost in a pleading tone. "I'm not accusing

Damon of anything. Detective Nowakowski and I are here solely because this is day two of the investigation. Leah was killed sometime yesterday afternoon. We were at the crime scene until late last night. Today, we have to start putting the pieces together. Interviewing the witnesses, family, loved ones, and acquaintances is standard procedure." He was about to remind her of the cardinal rule of homicide investigations: most people are killed by someone they know, but he thought better of it.

"That's fine. You put the pieces together. Just do it out of my house. And leave my son out of it. From now on, you contact us through our attorney."

"Yes, ma'am," Simon acquiesced. "Just who is your attorney?"

"My husband will advise you of that later. Good day, Detectives." She ushered them out of the house.

"Oh my," Rita blurted out on the sidewalk heading back down to their car. "We just got cut off at the pass."

"Temporary, at best. We'll get a crack at Damon. If Pollard or the crime scene techs come up with any useful physical evidence, we are entitled to get DNA evidence from Damon. If he really has nothing to do with it, which sounds likely, then his lawyer will be glad to cooperate with us to show us that trail is a dead end."

They headed back to the Homicide bureau downtown when Simon's cell rang. He always let Rita drive when they were together. That allowed him to concentrate on the case without the distractions of traffic. The caller was

Sergeant Ozzie McDaniel, a twenty-year veteran of the Department, one of the first-shift supervisors at District Four. He was pressed into the neighborhood canvass that Nowakowski ordered the night before. Bergdorf, at the end of his patrol career, worked briefly under McDaniel and knew him enough to know that he was solid. McDaniel worked the same "odd" side of the Marcus street, the houses with odd numbered addresses. Three doors down, he came upon the home of Edith and Ray Banks, the parents of Vernon Banks.

"Simon, you should come up here and talk to this guy soon," McDaniel referred to Vernon. "There's something weird about him." When Bergdorf asked what that was, McDaniel responded, "He's a forty-something-year-old grown man living in his parents' attic. Doesn't work, no visible means of support. Jumpy around me. You know the type. Don't like cops. He's been in trouble before. I guarantee it." Bergdorf respected McDaniel's instincts. He had spent his entire career on the streets, and he knew people. He could feel it in his bones when someone had something to hide.

Bergdorf told the sergeant he would head up to District Four and run a query on Mr. Banks and then stop by shortly after. It was quicker than going back to his office. At his old district building, Bergdorf and Nowakowski pulled up Banks's records. "Jackpot!" he exclaimed with a fist bump to Rita. Vernon Banks was forty-two years old and had a criminal record stretching back to juvie. They couldn't see those charges, as they were sealed, but the adult charges painted a

101

nasty and very unflattering picture of a sex offender and pedophile. Banks had been charged four times with assaulting teenage girls. The earliest charge got reduced down to a first-degree misdemeanor, but the later three charges were all felonies, most recently for rape. Banks served his last prison tour of duty for four years in the Mansfield Correctional Facility in north-central Ohio. No doubt, Bergdorf surmised, those were tough years. Child molesters don't fare well in prison. Banks was "rehabilitated" in prison, allegedly, and paroled. Unable to find a job with his record, he returned to his childhood home to live with his retired parents.

When the detectives rang the bell, Vernon answered the door. McDaniel warned him previously that the detectives would be there to talk to him and he'd better be there. McDaniel hung around on the street just in case Banks tried to make a dash for it.

"I know why you're here," Vernon told them. "It's about that girl up the street. Leah."

"That's right."

"I just want you to know. I had nothing to do with it."

They asked if they could come in off the porch, talk inside. Banks invited them in, proclaiming he had nothing to hide. Rita asked if they could look around his room. There was nothing inherently wrong with her request. Vernon lived there and certainly could give permission to the police to search his "suite" of rooms in the attic if he desired. Anything the detectives might find would then be admissible and not in violation of Banks's Fourth and

Fourteenth Amendments rights under the Constitution. They trudged up to the attic, which had a set of three rooms plus a bathroom. Simon thought it was bigger than a lot of apartments he had seen. Banks showed them around, including his police scanner radio, which sat on a table in his sitting room at the front of the house. That was how he spent a lot of his day, listening to the scanner.

Was that to remind himself of how lucky he was now that he was out of the system, Rita inquired. She noticed a Dell computer on the desk. Did he also like to surf the web, she asked. Look at porn? Little girls doing porn with middle-aged men like himself? Rita had zero tolerance for sex offenders. Banks wouldn't look her in the eye, she noted. He mumbled something about he didn't watch porn involving children, implicitly confirming that he did use his computer for more than reading the news on CNN. He didn't have a girlfriend; he admitted he didn't have any friends at all. He didn't have a job. Nobody would hire a felon like him. He just sat in his apartment all day long. His life was ruined. He had ruined his own life. He was just a shell now. He looked and sounded so pathetic, that she almost bought in to his story that he had nothing to do with Leah. Maybe he had PTSD after prison. Tough, she thought. Imagine what your victims have to deal with for the rest of their lives.

Yes, he had seen Leah in the neighborhood. No, he didn't think about her *that* way. He had been cured of his foibles in prison. Whether that was via the counseling he received from the therapists or the bedside, or rather in-bed, counseling he received from other inmates, Rita could not say. In any event, she didn't believe it. Once a pedophile, always a pedophile.

Where was he yesterday afternoon between noon and 4:00 p.m., Simon asked. Up in his front room, Banks responded. Did he leave the house at all? Yes, he took a daily walk in the neighborhood after lunch. Could his parents verify when he left and when he came back? No, he said. He used the back staircase and the rear door. Besides, his parents were down at the hospital for more testing of his mother's cancer. Did he walk by the Marcus house? Maybe he did, he admitted. Maybe hear Leah playing the piano? Spy on her through the parlor window?

No, nothing like that, Banks said. Sure, he had heard her play the piano before. She was really good! But he didn't think about her like *that*. Like a sexual being. He swore. The oath of a convicted felon held little cachet for either detective.

At the end of the morning of the thirteenth of April, the two detectives had two potential suspects, both of whom professed their innocence. So went the beginning of many a homicide investigation.

Later, the CSI techs would notify the detectives that they lifted Vernon Banks's fingerprints off of the window sill of the room in the Marcus house where Leah practiced piano on her Steinway. Banks's prints were part of his criminal record and easily identified. Bergdorf would later invite Banks down to give a DNA sample pursuant to a search warrant. He also obtained a warrant to search that Dell computer. The sick and disturbing images that Banks downloaded, and even categorized and indexed, made Rita want to vomit.

Chapter Fourteen

Autopsy

After the preliminary investigation at the murder scene, the coroner's office transported Leah's body to the Hamilton County Morgue, located in Clifton on Eden Avenue, part of the East Campus of the University of Cincinnati, very near to the Colleges of Medicine, Nursing, and Pharmacy. Normally, there would be quite a delay between a body taken to the coroner's office and when the autopsy would take place. However, everyone involved in this case felt a sense of urgency, so Dr. Pollard's schedule was cleared for the afternoon. Ben Marcus had already identified the body for Dr. Pollard.

Her naked body had already been weighed, measured, X-rayed and numerous photographs shot once again at the coroner's office. Leah was five feet three inches tall and weighed 110 pounds. The belts, bedclothes, and other evidence collected at the scene of the crime now resided, like the autopsy room, on the ground floor of the coroner's office awaiting examination, too. The five belts that the police found either on Leah's body or tied to the bed had been brought to the autopsy room, along with the cord that had been tied around Leah's neck. These were present so that Dr. Pollard could compare the marks on Leah's body with the various restraints most likely used to tie her down. The five belts all matched ligature marks on Leah's wrists and ankles. The head of the Greek statue matched the indentation on Leah's scalp.

Besides Pollard, Bergdorf, Nowakowski, and another physician, a pathologist from the coroner's office attended. Pollard suspected sexual assault, so she swabbed Leah's mouth, vagina, and rectum. She did collect semen. She examined Leah's fingernails closely. She scraped the nails as she saw residue suggestive that Leah had fought back, perhaps scratching her assailant or assailants with her fingernails. The X-rays confirmed Pollard's suspicion that the wound on Leah's head was nasty and quite a bleeder, but there was no skull fracture.

Bergdorf had seen plenty of autopsies during his career. He knew the routine. Even though the temperature rose into the eighties, he wore a sweater. The air conditioners in the room pumped torrents of cold air through the vents. Yet, Bergdorf's anger burned bright and clean, like the very surgical instruments as they sat sterilized on a pad prior to being used to carve open Leah's body. Looking at her beautiful form desecrated by the "Y" incision, he felt a quiet fury build inside him that he would nail the bastard who murdered Leah.

Pollard worked swiftly but expertly. Stomach contents revealed the masticated remains of lunch; Leah's bladder still retained a small amount of urine and that was collected for toxicology along with blood samples. Pollard recalled the petechiae in the eyes that suggested strangulation as the cause of death. Leah's death certificate used the standard language: "This was a homicide, by party or parties unknown."

Pollard's report listed strangulation as the mechanical cause of death. The cord wrapped around her neck bit deeply into the tissue, bruising it as well as the tissue internally in the larynx and trachea. The mechanism of death was combined asphyxia with venous congestion. Without a witness to Leah's death, Pollard was unable to give an exact time of death but listed it as occurring on the afternoon of Thursday, April 12. Couching her language in the standard opinion lingo used by medical examiners, Pollard posited within a reasonable degree of medical certainty that Leah Marcus died on Thursday, April 12, 2001, and that the manner of death was homicide.

She sent semen samples, fingernail scrapings, and pubic hair from the comforter that covered Leah's body as well as her bed, and some of the vacuumed material collected from the floors of the Marcus home to the coroner's upstairs laboratory for analysis. Those results would not hit Pollard's and Bergdorf's desks for several more weeks. Less than four hours after she commenced the autopsy, Pollard finished it.

Chapter Fifteen

First Reactions

News of Leah's murder hit the newspapers, at least briefly, on Friday the thirteenth. My own short article was buried at the bottom of page two of the Metro section. The riots still held sway with the prime real estate, the front page and the first page of the Metro section.

Tory Maxwell's mother saw my article and showed it to her daughter. That set off a flurry of telephone calls, so that by dinner time on Friday, most of the Walnut Hills community knew of Leah's death. Tory still recalls her reaction when her mother showed her the article. "I didn't believe. It couldn't be true. That girl had the vitality of life. She was going to live to be a hundred and still rocking the nursing home with show tunes on the little spinet piano in the lunchroom." Like so many people I interviewed for this book, Tory just refused to believe what she read. It was classic Elizabeth Kubler Ross and the five stages of grief, the first being denial. Shock followed denial.

Rebecca Stonecraft, the Marcuses' next-door neighbor, told me she put her hand to her mouth because she thought she might vomit. Putting her hand there, she figured, would force the spew back down her throat, perhaps, thereby, making the news go back from whence it came to the day before, before Leah died, so that if she opened her kitchen window, she might still hear Leah playing the piano.

Sarah Winters, Leah's piano teacher at school, recalls laughing when a colleague telephoned her with the news, thinking the call a practical joke. After being assured that it was not, tears welled up in her eyes and then poured down her face.

For all those people who heard the news, devastating as it was, to then learn that someone murdered Leah was almost too much to bear. Adults knew that kids sometimes died. Those unfortunate souls developed cancer or some rare disease like cystic fibrosis, or they died in drunken car accidents. But nobody in Leah's world knew anyone who died the victim of a homicide. That news seared their souls. Several adults told me they harkened back to a 1977 Billy Joel song they heard as young adults, but which their kids didn't really know: "Only the Good Die Young." It was so consummately unfair that Leah's life force would be snuffed out young and in such a manner. Incomprehensible was a word oft repeated. Leah's peers had an even more difficult time dealing with the news. Teenagers believe they are immortal; they cannot conceive of their own death nor that of their friends. "You could have told me a meteor hit downtown, and I would have been more prone to believe that than that Leah was dead," Tory told me.

Sarah and Ben Marcus could barely move, yet they had to. The police evicted them from their own home with just a suitcase each. Sarah called their son David, who attended the University of Chicago, and gave him a sanitized version, telling him he needed to make arrangements to come home. She then called her parents, who lived in Amberley Village, a wealthy community adjacent to the northeast corner of Cincinnati, and passed on the news. Her father headed one of Cincinnati's reform temples and would preside over Leah's funeral service in just a few short days. The Marcuses stayed with her parents for a couple of days until the police allowed them back into their own house.

After the autopsy, the coroner's office released Leah's body and effects to her family. Ben Marcus called the only Jewish funeral home in town; its representatives transported her body to their facility. Jewish custom is to bury the dead as soon after death as possible. Custom also mandates a closed casket ceremony. Ben, still thinking of the cord he saw wrapped tightly around his daughter's throat, thanked the Lord for small graces. He could not conceive having to look at her bruised neck and her face. He never wanted to see that sight again, yet knew he would never live another day without waking to that nightmarish vision. Nor did he want any gawking at the funeral. Leah's friends would be there, possibly other family members, lingering over the casket, peering in to view her throat even though he would pick out a high-necked dress to cover the wound.

He knew how an autopsy was performed, how the medical examiner makes an intermastoid incision, cutting the head from ear to ear, folding back the skin of the face, inside out over the front of the face to allow access to the cranium. He knew, as an ex-prosecutor who attended autopsies, the thousand RPM whine of the power saw as it cleaves open the cranial vault, the ripping and popping sounds the brain makes as it is dissected from the spinal cord and the meninges and lifted out of the head for examination. He had no idea how a mortician could fix those wounds to make them look more lifelike. What a joke, he told me years later. That a mortician could possibly make her look more lifelike. Like she was sleeping.

Leah's funeral was Monday the sixteenth, three days after Tim Thomas's. Hundreds of people came, although they all couldn't obtain seats for the service at the funeral home. Family took precedence, so many of Leah's peers stood around in the parking lot, the girls in their dresses, comfortable in their heels and talking low, although a few laughs broke out over fun recollections of Leah. The boys stood as awkward stiffs in their suits. Unlike the girls, they only got dressed up for three occasions—funerals, weddings, and prom.

Sarah's father, the Rabbi Manny Schifrin, conducted the service. His ceremony included all the standard Jewish liturgy, including the Mourner's Kaddish, the prayer uttered by Jews for countless centuries and which is supposed to both console the survivors while still exalting the glory of God.

One verse of the prayer reads:
Exalted and hallowed be God's great name
in the world which God created, according to
plan.
May God's majesty be revealed in the days of our
lifetime
and the life of all Israel—speedily, imminently, to
which we say Amen.

Sarah grew up hearing that prayer at
services at the temple, including those for her
own dead relatives. She knew the melodic verses
in Hebrew by heart, which sounded even more
mellifluent than translated in English. She
thought she understood their meaning. She could
not fathom God's glory in striking down a young
woman with so much promise poised to begin
the prime of her life. Where's the glory in
crushing us as we would step on an insect? Does
my ability to squash a beetle make me a god?
Show me the exaltation there. So when it was
time to say Kaddish for her own daughter, she
inwardly railed—if that be sacrilege, so be it—
that in death we still extol God's glory. Someone
had killed her daughter, and no glory was owed
to him. From that day forward, Sarah Marcus
never would step into a temple again. Years later,
she would turn to Buddhism for spiritual solace.

Damon Allbright, accompanied by his
parents, also attended. They sat in the last row of
seats. The Allbrights knew the Marcuses; their
son, after all, had been going out with Leah for
almost two years. They didn't know them well,
but they had shared several family meals
together, such as Thanksgiving and Passover at

the Marcus home and Christmas dinner at the Allbright home. I had the sense that the Marcuses didn't disapprove of Damon, but only wished, secretly, that he was white. That conviction of mine did not emanate from anything any of the Marcuses ever told me. Rather, it came from the Allbrights when I interviewed them years after the events that took place here occurred.

Delores and Othello Allbright are optimistic people. They are also realistic. While they want a world not tainted by racism, they can feel it everywhere around them in the white world, can glean a white person's racism from a macroaggression. One instance that Delores cited was at Passover dinner in the year 2000 at the Marcus house. After dinner, Ben and Othello sat in the Marcus study, talking about some case or another of Ben's. Othello, while an educated man, had not trained as a lawyer, but he followed Ben's strategies for the case well and offered suggestions that Ben found cogent. At one point, Ben told Othello in this conversation, Delores told me, that "[w]hen I look at you, I don't see a person of color." Ben Marcus uttered a classic macroaggression, a demeaning refusal to even acknowledge the race of another, and implicitly suggesting that the white race is inherently superior.

So the Allbrights chose to sit in the rear seats, not only because they sensed the Marcuses inherent racism, but because, as Delores explained it, she could already sense that Damon was becoming a target of the investigation. She had gleaned that from Bergdorf's questioning at her house three days ago. When she and Othello talked with Damon over the weekend, they realized that the breakup would loom large in the investigation; perhaps, she had correctly surmised, the Marcuses already told the police about the breakup. They went through the receiving line after the service, issued their heartfelt condolences, awkwardly hugged Sarah and Ben, and made a quick exit.

Sarah later told me that she could not believe the unmitigated gall that Damon, and by association his parents, showed by coming to the funeral. Sarah would come to believe Damon was the Satanic architect of Leah's death. Damon, her daughter's boyfriend and no doubt lover, yet also her killer, her *murderer*, and there he was at the funeral offering his compassion. Later, thinking back on it, a Sophoclean rage overtook her and she wanted to rip his bloody eyeballs from their very sockets and strangle him with his own optic cords.

Chapter Sixteen

Alibis

Bergdorf and Nowakowski attended Leah's funeral. They knew that sometimes a murderer takes grim and sick satisfaction out of going to or watching from afar the funeral of his victim. They also followed the cortege *en route* to the Jewish cemetery in Montgomery, a bedroom community north and east of Cincinnati, where Leah would be interred for eternity. Or at least until her resurrection, Simon thought, in accordance with Jewish belief. He had seen so much death over the years and had his own faith challenged that he thought it more likely that Leah would lay there for eternity long before she would ever come back to life. They saw no one, other than Damon, of course, who aroused their suspicion.

The detectives did not have the weekend off between their Friday interrogations and the Monday funeral. They worked the case on Saturday and Sunday. People killed fifty-five other people in Cincinnati in the year 2001, and the team had more than enough work to keep busy with current cases. When not actively involved in a current investigation, they would break out cold case files.

Leah's murder investigation went right to the top of their workload. This was the pattern of their professional life. Feast or famine. They silently prayed for famine, not because they wanted less work, but because less murders meant less heartbreak for all parties involved. By Friday evening, the police chief himself had called them into his office to expound the, by then, obvious political implications of this case and spurred them on to clear it promptly. Just what they needed, Bergdorf told Nowakowski— pressure from the top.

After the autopsy, they returned to their offices and started work to clear obvious potential suspects—the parents of Leah and Damon. They worked to identify where the parents were on the date of the murder, especially in the hours between noon and four. Othello Allbright spent the day at the church offices, Sarah at her Wellspring offices, and Ben spent the entire day, until Sarah called him, at his law office. Only Delores did not have a job, and she had lunch with a friend. The detectives would verify with in-person interviews that these people were where they appeared to have been. Simon had very low suspicion for the parents, but he was not going to leave any loose ends untied. A good detective, like a good criminal, never does.

He also ran criminal background checks on all four parents. He found that both Sarah and Delores had been ticketed for a few minor traffic violations. Othello had been charged twice with disorderly conduct, both cases dismissed. Simon suspected these were related to his community activism and would verify it later. Ben's record was clear except for a long-ago case involving a hit and run accident that was dismissed without a conviction.

Simon also polled his homicide colleagues to see if they had any current or past cases with scenarios similar to Leah's. When the answers returned uniformly negative, he placed a call to an FBI contact. He wanted to know if the Feds had any information on serial killers who acted with a *modus operandi* similar to the Marcus murder. His contact promised to check and call him back, but it would take some time. Bergdorf never wanted to pre-judge a case. His instincts told him to go with the percentages, namely that Leah was killed by someone she knew and trusted. Otherwise, the door to the Marcus home would never have been opened voluntarily, especially during such a tense time as the riots. But just in case, he worked the "stranger did it" angle. Simon Bergdorf knew how to hedge a bet.

Over the course of the weekend, the detectives confirmed that the parents had alibis for their whereabouts during the crucial hours in question. Dozens of people could attest to Ben Marcus's presence at his law office on Thursday, including not only his employees, but independent parties, such as the court reporter taking the deposition, the adverse party, and his attorneys. Clearly, Ben was where he said he was. Sarah's whereabouts were also easily established, although, there were no independent persons other than Sarah's employees, and the office had over forty such persons present the afternoon of the twelfth. It seemed unlikely that all these people would lie for Sarah. Plus, the manner of Leah's death suggested a male was the person who committed the crime. The entire panoply of sexual aggression and bondage indicated a man intent on humiliating and torturing a woman in a very specific, gender-based manner. Usually, these were sociopaths with low self-esteem who held grudges against attractive young women, perhaps because they could never acquire one in the usual method of courtship, Simon thought. Or the victim reminded him of the girl in high school who turned him down for a date or his boss who failed to recognize his contributions to the company. Any perceived injustice would serve as a valid excuse to exact retribution in such a degrading way on some unlikely stranger. Or Leah might just have been a target of opportunity.

The hardest person to verify an alibi for was Delores Allbright. Her friend confirmed they had lunch downtown between noon and one. The companion mentioned that Delores intended to go shopping while she was downtown. The detectives' inquiry had been shut down tightly on Friday by Delores herself, so they had no opportunity to hear from her where she was or what she had been doing. By the time they had that opportunity later, the investigation had taken a complete detour when other evidence would surface, pointing the detectives in a different direction.

The one person they definitely wanted to interview was Vernon Banks. They came calling for him again on Sunday afternoon. By Sunday morning, the detectives confirmed that Banks left his fingerprints on the window sill of the room where Leah played piano. That was enough to get a judge known to be friendly to the police to issue a search warrant for Vernon's house.

Bergdorf and Nowakowski showed up in the afternoon with a team of other detectives and forensic personnel. After a two-hour search of the third-floor apartment, they found no incriminating evidence, no trophies like a ring from Leah's jewelry box or a locket of hair. But the detectives found a digital camera with an SD card. They took the camera and Banks's computer with them and brought Banks down to police headquarters where they recorded his interview.

Bergdorf let me watch the interview tape, and I did, in its entirety. Banks was forty-two at the time, and looked, apologies to Fred Rogers, a little like the namesake host of the old PBS television show—a middle-aged, harmless man with dark hair parted on the left and droopy shoulders. Down the hall, a crime tech looked at Banks's computer and camera. He would later interrupt the interview to show the detectives what he had found.

"You know why you're here, right, Vernon?" Bergdorf inquired.

"I'm guessing it's about that Leah girl."

"Your guess is correct."

"Did you have anything to do with *that Leah girl's* death, Vernon?" Banks shook his head. "Because if you did, and there's an explanation for it, a reasonable explanation, I might be able to get the prosecutor to take it easy on you."

"No. I swear. I had nothing to do with it."

"In cases like this, here in Hamilton County, the jurors and judges, well, they don't like murderers. And child rapists. Those kind of men, they give them the death penalty. You know that, don't you?" Banks looked away from Simon. "I want justice for Leah, Vernon. But that doesn't mean I want her murderer to get executed. Maybe there was a reason. An escalation that led to her getting killed. Maybe an accident. Maybe she taunted you. The size of your penis or something that made you mad. Killing in a fit of rage might get you off the death penalty."

"I'm telling you. It wasn't me. I was home. All day."

"All day? You never left the house? Didn't you tell me the other day you did take a walk that afternoon?"

Banks shrugged his droopy shoulders. "Well, I did go for a walk in the afternoon." Nowakowski's and Bergdorf's eyes locked on each other's at that comment.

"Where did you walk to?"

"Around the neighborhood."

"Did you, by chance, walk by the Marcus house?"

"I might have."

"By chance, did you walk up to it? Say on the front or back porch? Or, maybe, peer in the window when Leah was practicing the piano?"

"No."

"No? Are you sure you don't want to amend that answer, Vernon?" Banks shook his head again. "Because I know you were at that house." Now it was Banks's turn to lock eyes with the detective. "Yep. I've got your fingerprints there. You want to tell me about that?"

As I watched the interview, I could practically see the little wheels in Vernon Banks's head turn. He knew he had been caught, but he couldn't quite tell what exactly Bergdorf had on him. Fingerprints, where? I can see how the detectives thought that piece of information both incriminating and damaging. But, in retrospect, I can see Banks's surprise because he knew he had peeped into her window, but he also knew he didn't kill her. Yet, how to explain that to the detectives without partially implicating himself. He had probably peeped several times, and he was trying to recount when that last time was.

The crime technicians lifted numerous fingerprints from inside the house, and specifically within Leah's bedroom. Most of them remained unidentified. It would take some time to match all the prints to their owners' hands. Except for Ben Marcus's. As a lawyer, he submitted his fingerprints to the authorities when he sought admission to the Bar, so his prints had long been on file. What the techs never found were Vernon Banks's prints *inside* the Marcus home. Bergdorf also knew that piece of information at the time he interviewed Banks.

"What I'm trying to figure is, why, if you wore gloves inside the house, didn't you also wear them outside?" Bergdorf told me it was a calculated risk to let Banks know they didn't have prints from the inside of the home, but he wasn't going to try tricking Banks on that issue.

The courts had at times reversed convictions found upon overzealous lying on the part of police to suspects. Banks insisted he had nothing to do with Leah's death.

An hour into the interview, the technician looking at Banks's computer interrupted the session and asked Bergdorf and Nowakowski to join him down the hall. They left the room for twenty minutes. You can see Banks pacing the room, like a caged animal at the zoo, sweating off pent up energy, fear, and adrenaline. When they returned, Nowakowski took over.

"I thought you said you never thought of Leah that way?" she asked.

"What way?"

"Like a sex object."

"I didn't."

"It doesn't appear you ever stop thinking about teenage girls, Vernon. Look what we found on your computer." She showed him images they found on his computer. The computer screen sits with its back to the camera, so I was not able to see those pictures. But Nowakowski and Bergdorf assured me they found over six thousand images of porn, much of it bondage, S&M, and the like, involving young women, maybe teenagers, maybe of legal age, maybe not. But they also found hundreds of images of pre-pubescent girls involved in sexual acts with grown men. Those images would land Vernon Banks back in jail for another prison term.

What the detectives never found were any pictures of Leah Marcus, alive or dead.

Chapter Seventeen

Keith Isaiah Jones

After Leah's funeral and burial, Bergdorf and Nowakowski regrouped at their office in the Homicide bureau's office on Lynn Street downtown. They split up a list of witnesses who could verify the whereabouts of Ben and Sarah Marcus and Othello Allbright. They spent the next day and the next morning interviewing these people at their places of work, cementing the alibis for three out of the four of Leah's and Damon's parents.

They wanted to get out of the office for lunch. They drove from their office in Queensgate to downtown. They parked in a lot on Central Parkway right past the third Hamilton County Courthouse. The first two succumbed to fires. The day was warm, bright, pretty, and they opted to buy hot dogs and Cokes from a street vendor, then sat on a bench in the shade of the courthouse to eat and talk.

As they talked, a tall African American man exited the building and, glancing over at them, doing a double-take, walked over to them. Even over the noise of traffic and passersby, his deep, baritone voice boomed. "Detectives! It's been a while," he greeted them.

His name was Keith Isaiah Jones. He stood six foot four, athletic still in his mid-fifties then, and people made way for him when he walked down the sidewalk. Jones was the premier criminal defense attorney for people of color in Cincinnati at the time. He was also an ordained minister. In that capacity, he knew many of the preachers around town, stood side-by-side with them on marches and other community occasions. Those preachers funneled a large number of clients for Isaiah's practice. His advertisements appeared everywhere in print, on the radio, and on television. His famous tagline was, "Call me if you need me!" While most of his clients paid him in cash, he more often than not would take cases by appointment from the court or handle cases for people he felt needed representation for free if they could not afford his services.

In winter, he would stride into the courthouse with a full-length fur coat and a large hat, which made him appear almost seven feet tall. If you were black and in trouble with the system and didn't need a public defender because you could afford a lawyer, you hired Jones. He was an exceptional attorney, notwithstanding his occasional grandstanding for the media, his advertising, and his once-in-awhile antics in court. No one at the prosecutor's office took him lightly. He found that even with predominately white juries, his story would resonate with them—police brutality, sloppy procedural work by detectives, beat cops, and CSI people. Many of his white jurors were not rich, and while Hamilton County was a notoriously law and order community, when Jones spun a tale of police corruption, his notions of fairness and decency made inroads with jurors. White or black, you could relate to his story of the great state of Ohio beating up on a downtrodden poor person. Plus, the high bar of the criminal standard of proof, finding evidence beyond a reasonable doubt to hold a defendant guilty, worked to his advantage.

Bergdorf told me he thought Jones was there just to chitchat or, perhaps, talk about an old case. They had no current cases pending. The conversation didn't go as expected.

"Simon, I've picked up a new client. We'd like to come down to the station and talk with you and Detective Nowakowski about it." Jones knew Bergdorf since the time Bergdorf was a beat cop and ticketed Jones for a failure to maintain assured clear distance traffic charge way back in the day when the young officer patrolled the streets of District Four. Jones lived in North Avondale and, on a snowy winter day, slammed on the brakes but skidded into the rear end of the car in front of him stopped at a traffic light. Definitely not a case of "driving while black." They had worked on opposite sides of other cases over the years, even as Bergdorf became a detective and then, more recently, a homicide detective. Isaiah, as he preferred to be called, knew Simon Bergdorf well enough to greet him by first name. Nowakowski, though, was another matter. He didn't know her so well and, as was his custom with all others, promoting mutual respect, addressed her by her title.

Simon told me he doesn't believe in coincidences. His antennae twitched when Jones mentioned a new client. Emphasis on the 'new.' Simon and Rita weren't working any "new" cases other than the Marcus murder, so Simon had a hunch this new client had something to do with Leah's case. "We have a few interviews to do this afternoon. We caught a new case."

"I heard," Jones said.

"We could be back at the station at say, 5:00 p.m. Would that work for you and your client?"

"Excellent. See you then. Enjoy your lunch. Oh, and Simon?"

"Yes?"

"Watch those hot dogs. All that cholesterol isn't safe for a body." He laughed his amiable, booming laugh and walked south towards his law office.

Regrouping at the office, Rita and Simon talked about who the client could be. Rita voted for Damon Allbright, and Simon agreed. Promptly at five, Jones walked through the doors and asked to see the detectives. As they stepped off the elevator, Simon and Rita exchanged a knowing glance, as Damon stood there at Jones's side.

The meeting started in one of the nicer interview rooms, almost a conference room. Jones declined a videotaped meeting; Damon would not be making any statements. There is no primary record of that "interview," but Simon wrote extensive notes both in his note cards and his investigative file. His memory seemed sharp about the meeting even without referring to his note cards.

"Isaiah said, after we all settled around the conference table, that Damon's family hired him to represent Damon. They, the family, believed Damon was a 'person of interest' in the investigation. No such announcement had been made to the media. Jones wanted to confirm if that was true. It was, of course, so far as the entire 'person of interest' label has any meaning. It has no legal meaning, and generally refers to someone who law enforcement refers to when the person hasn't been arrested or charged with a crime. But it can also be used to mean a witness cooperating with the police, a person who may have information concerning the investigation or has certain characteristics that merit further attention. It was that latter quality that Jones was hinting at.

"Rita and I, and therefore the Department, had made no informal determination that Damon was a person of interest, but certainly we wanted to talk to him and we wanted to examine his body (scrapings had been taken from under Leah's fingernails; did she slash at her assailant?) and take DNA and hair samples. If Damon was Leah's killer, and if she had scratched him with her nails, then the wounds on his body would be healing five days after the event. Damon was eighteen years old; teens' bodies heal quickly from wounds. So, basically, yes, Damon was a person of interest, whether Rita and I had actually used that term amongst ourselves."

Jones knew that the police had a right to take samples from Damon's body, such as hair samples and a DNA swab, once they got a search warrant. Taking pictures of his body, since he was not under arrest, was another matter. Making a show for Damon's benefit, Jones told the detectives that Damon chose to exercise his Constitutional right to remain silent. He acknowledged that Damon was aware that the police were collecting physical evidence from the victim and the crime scene and had a legal interest in testing Damon's DNA. Since Damon had nothing to hide, they would consent to a DNA sample. Simon called in a crime technician who collected hair samples and swabbed Damon's cheek. Damon balked at letting anyone examine his body, which he assumed meant stripping down to do so. Rita let a jab fly, asking him if he had nothing to hide, if he wasn't there in Leah's bedroom when she was killed, then there would be no wound on his body even if fingernail evidence showed she had scratched her attacker. Jones volleyed back that even if Damon had a mark on his body, it could just as easily have come from an injury at a pickup basketball game, nullifying any point in examining his naked body. Rita said it didn't really matter, because if it was Damon's DNA under Leah's fingernails, and in her mouth, vagina, and rectum, then they had Damon dead to right anyway.

At that point, neither Damon nor Isaiah knew that Leah had been sexually assaulted. Again, Bergdorf and Nowakowski noted Damon's look of horror when he realized the true circumstances of Leah's death. He wasn't exactly thrilled that Rita let those facts slip. Rita, he knew, was very protective of her sexual assault victims; she had many times verbally lambasted suspects for how they treated the women in their life. She wasn't then thinking that Damon was the killer, but her protective instincts took over. She had seen far too many victims of sexual assault, some of them murdered by their boyfriends, their lovers, their husbands, or their ex- any of those categories. More of these women were African American than white.

Simon knew that Damon was the star basketball player at school. But he didn't want to paint him into the same celebrity entitlement category as, say, O. J. Simpson. He still wanted to give Damon the benefit of doubt, still found his denial sincere and figured that his parents had the means to hire a lawyer like Jones and why not protect their son's interests if they could.

Simon often wondered if she had been a victim at some time in her past. She never shared that with him, and in any event, Leah's murder occurred long before the #MeToo movement gained traction, so speaking up about sexual assault wasn't nearly as commonplace in 2001. Simon knew that Damon and his lawyer were going to hear about the sex crime aspect of the case sooner or later if Damon were somehow implicated by his DNA, so there was no point in berating Rita over the slip.

The forensic people sent the samples from the crime scene to the crime lab on Thursday, the night of the murder. Those results would come back within the next few weeks. The matchup samples to exclude, or include, Damon as a suspect left for the same lab five days later.

Neither Simon nor Rita wanted to take a bet on the outcome of that analysis. In the meantime, they had plenty of work left to do on the case.

Chapter Eighteen

Interlude

On Wednesday, April 18, the CPD sent Damon Allbright's DNA and hair samples to the county crime lab. Five long weeks went by before the results came back to Bergdorf and Nowakowski. Normally, the lab would return the analysis within a week, perhaps two at most. But the inopportune departure of Dr. Patel, the DNA "guru" at the lab, who had returned to his native India for a three-week vacation, put the analysis on hold. Everyone involved in the investigation wanted the analysis done quick, but they all agreed it had to be done right so that it would hold up in court when the time came. Patel was the man to do the job, so Damon's DNA sat in the office awaiting Patel's return. When he returned to work, he compared Damon's DNA to the DNA and other items taken from Leah's body and the crime scene. In the interim, the detectives continued working the investigation.

They picked up a tantalizing trail concerning the mystery woman that Alice Bowman, the Marcuses' neighbor, reported seeing driving down the street, parking, and walking back to Leah's home. Security cameras captured photos of a dark colored sedan, perhaps a Toyota Camry, driving south on

Reading Road with a female driver with long, light-colored hair and sunglasses. The time stamps on the security cameras coincided with the time frame that Alice Bowman said she saw the woman. A security camera at the Belvedere Condominiums, a high-rise building at Reading and Clinton Springs, also captured an image of this car as it turned from Reading onto Clinton Springs, a mere couple of very short blocks from Burton Woods Lane. The technicians who viewed the images could not obtain a license plate number from the grainy images. The pictures showed a shadow in the passenger seat that may or may not have been another person.

Bergdorf and Nowakowski spoke with dozens of Leah's classmates, teachers and other school personnel, and acquaintances. The detectives tried to form a more nuanced view of who Leah was, who she hung out with, who were her friends or enemies, if she had any. They worked on getting a timeline of Leah's whereabouts for the week before she died, to glean any information of someone she may have come across who might have wanted to harm her. These various interviews uncovered little that helped the investigators. Leah lived a charmed life right up until the moment it ended. They checked a log of calls from her cell phone to see who she was talking or texting with.

While the riots had ended, the aftermath had not. The media focused on the damage to the city and what could be done to fix the culture of police interaction with citizens. Nevertheless, the story of Leah's murder started to gain traction. On Thursday, April 19, one week after her death,

Lieutenant Horstmeyer called a press conference in response to media inquiries. I attended that event at a conference room in District One, the police headquarters building. He added a few details, salacious ones that reporters duly noted in their articles or television reports, about Leah being found naked, bound, and sexually assaulted. The perpetrator, or perpetrators, had bludgeoned her on the head but killed her by strangulation. The police had no suspects at this time but diligently worked all angles. The police collected DNA samples from the crime scene (there was no mention of the DNA harvested from the cheeks of either Vernon Banks or Damon Allbright) and sent them to the crime lab for analysis. When the results came back, they would search databases of DNA previously collected from crime scenes or suspects on file. The problem with that approach, I questioned, was if the suspect or suspects were not already in the DNA database, then how would that help identify Leah's killer? Horstmeyer acknowledged the possibility that the perpetrator's DNA might not be in the system yet. But it might be, or it might turn up shortly. When pressed to answer how it might end up there shortly, I again inquired if the police had any suspects. Otherwise, it might end up there not at all, or years from now, but why did he use the word 'shortly'? He deflected by saying that he used a figure of speech, a hope, a wish that they would shortly have an answer.

Other reporters wanted to know if Leah died the victim of a serial killer on the loose. Horstmeyer replied that the Department had no indication that there was a new serial killer on the loose. Her death did not resemble any known homicides the Department worked on. They were checking with the FBI to see if they had information of a serial killer using that *modus operandi*. The lieutenant repeated the oft-noted mantra of the police that most homicide victims are murdered by someone they know, and this was the emphasis of the investigation. Nevertheless, they would consider all possibilities.

Ben Marcus attended the press conference. He spoke with Horstmeyer, Bergdorf, and Nowakowski after the reporters left. They gave him more details than they gave the press. They told him they had harvested DNA from Damon and from a neighbor, whom they declined to identify, but who they said was a known sex offender. Marcus had a week to recover from the shock of his daughter's death. Now, he was in full-on professional, manic overdrive, driven lawyer mode. He demanded to know who this person was, who could be living on his street with no notice from the authorities that a sex offender lived near to children. His children.

Bergdorf told me that he let Horstmeyer take the lead in answering Marcus's questions. After all, Horstmeyer was the supervising detective and his boss. Plus, it was fun to watch him squirm like a bacteria under Ben Marcus's microscope. Horstmeyer cautioned Marcus that the police had no evidence that connected this person to the murder. In a few weeks, when the DNA reports came back, if this person matched up, he would be arrested and his identity disclosed. Otherwise, he had a right to privacy, as well. Privacy, Marcus wanted to know, what about the rights of parents whose children lived on the same street? How could they protect their children from a shadow child exploiter who lived like a vampire, since apparently nobody was entitled to know who he even was?

Ben Marcus decided on the spot after Horstmeyer's vacillation that he would take the matter into his own hands. He would take a leave of absence from work effective the following Monday. With his newfound spare time, he would press the police department to do their job, consider, he told me, hiring a private investigator of his own if he felt it would be useful, and started travelling I-71 north to Columbus to lobby legislators to pass a sex offender notification law for Ohio. Ben Marcus's tireless efforts on behalf of Ohio crime victims resulted in the passage of Ohio's sex offender registration law.

The week after the riots, kids went back to school. Places of business reopened. A tepid sense of normalcy returned to Cincinnati; although, people still felt ill at ease. Race relations, never great, did not improve. The police tried to be more circumspect with the use of force in encounters with African Americans.

For Damon Allbright and Vernon Banks, life went on, but in an on-hold status. They both didn't sleep well pending the return of the DNA reports. Vernon had been to prison; he didn't relish going back. Damon had no idea what prison was like, but he didn't want to find out. He likened it, to me, years after the trial, to a movie he once he saw. In the film, a small propeller plane has engine trouble. The motor sputters, stops, restarts, sputters again, and finally cuts out for good. For a moment, there is dead silence in the cabin of the aircraft. Then a little bit of a whistling noise starts. Then the plane dips nose down, accelerating in a whining free fall to earth. Those days before the DNA report, he was in that hushed aircraft cabin, still flying, but scared that the bottom was just about to drop out.

Chapter Nineteen

Arrest

Damon Allbright was a good kid. I have expounded on the hagiography of St. Leah, if you will pardon the mixing of religious metaphors involving a Jewish saint. But let's not forget that Damon Allbright was a fine young man prior to the happenings of April 2001. Damon had a 3.7 GPA at Walnut Hills. He was the star point guard for the basketball team. His singing voice was otherworldly. Some thought his voice almost as good as Leah's piano playing. He sang in his father's church choir, in various groups at the high school such as Glee Club and the *Hills Are Alive,* an *a cappella* group, and at practically any gathering of friends he found himself at.

He was well-liked by peers and teachers alike. He was respectful, addressing adults as 'sir' or 'ma'am.' Unlike Leah, he didn't know exactly what he would study in college or what his career trajectory would be. But those who knew him said his charisma, his smarts, his decency, and his work ethic would take him far, be it in business, the arts, or politics. During summers, he served as a camp counselor at the Mt. Carmel Baptist Church camp where he taught the younger kids, girls too, how to play basketball. He participated in the church youth group, had gone on missions to Africa during parts of summers when he didn't volunteer at camp.

The only time he contacted the criminal justice system was for two speeding tickets as a sixteen-year-old, minor infractions not dissimilar from that of males of any race once they get a driver's license and a car. When he interacted with the police, he was polite. In return, the officers told him, gently, to slow down and handed Damon his tickets. The officers, one white, the other black, had no idea who his father was. They simply responded to his being respectful of them as police officers.

During the weeks waiting for the DNA results to come back, Bergdorf and Nowakowski kept working the investigation as best they could. They identified most of the fingerprints found in the Marcus house and especially Leah's bedroom. Those prints belonged to Leah herself, Ben, Sarah, and her brother David. The police knew that David wasn't involved; they just needed to rule out his previously unknown set of prints. Others belonged to Leah's girlfriends and the (white) cleaning lady who took care of the Marcus home every week on Fridays. Damon left his fingerprints all over Leah's room. Still, there were random prints unidentified. The most intriguing of these, the forensics technician found partial prints on the bronze statue from Greece that the assailant used to bludgeon Leah's head. Bergdorf's "murder book" notes stated that the investigators found no set of full prints in the house that matched the partial print on the statue. Isaiah Jones would hammer these issues at trial.

On Thursday, May 24, the crime lab emailed the results to Bergdorf and the medical examiner. A hard copy would follow by mail, but the homicide detective had what he needed, but not necessarily what he wanted. He called Nowakowski to his desk to read the report. He waited for her to arrive before he opened the attachment.

What appeared to be pubic hairs on the bedclothes, particularly the comforter that Sarah Marcus covered her daughter's naked body with, seemed to match Damon's. Light microscopy identified the hairs as human, of African ancestry. Additional hairs from a human head, again of African ancestry, were found on the bedclothes. This alone suggested Damon as a suspect, but only one of thousands of African American males in Greater Cincinnati. By itself, it was circumstantial evidence but hardly the sort of evidence that a prosecution would rely upon as its main source of physical evidence.

One red herring concerned the DNA scraped from under Leah's fingernails. That DNA did not match Damon's. Was there another assailant involved? Had Leah scratched another person from some other incident of self-defense prior to the date of her death?

However, the DNA taken from Damon's cheek matched that from the semen taken from Leah's body. Unless Damon had a monozygotic (identical) twin, then the odds were that he was the one and only person on the planet who sexually assaulted Leah. The detectives looked at each other with stunned looks on their faces. They had both believed Damon's expressions of

140

shock when he learned that she was dead, the victim of murder. Yet again, he exhibited not only surprise but horror when Rita told him that the killer sexually assaulted Leah. Other than his breakup with Leah, there was nothing to suggest his relationship with her was fraught with violence or danger. The leap of faith from a spurned boyfriend to enraged rapist spanned a large chasm. But getting from sexual assault to murder entailed a smaller leap of faith. The DNA evidence damned Damon. That would be the prosecutor's burden, but certainly they had Damon for the rape.

Bergdorf told Nowakowski he thought something must be missing here, unless Damon was such a sociopath that he could fake surprise as he did. But if he was a sociopath, the rest of his background didn't add up. Sociopaths are self-centered; they don't care about people the way Damon obviously did.

The detectives told Lieutenant Horstmeyer the results of the DNA tests. It was just after one in the afternoon. They wanted to pick Damon up, or better yet, have Isaiah Jones bring him down that day. That way, he would maybe only have to spend a night in jail; he could get a court hearing the next day and perhaps be bailed out pending trial. Horstmeyer nixed that idea. He wanted the arrest to be done late Friday, so that Damon would have to spend the entire weekend in jail before having a hearing in front of a judge. Besides, with the Memorial Day holiday about to start, Damon would miss the Saturday morning arraignment court and would have to wait all the way until the following

Tuesday before he could get a bail hearing. Plus, it would be great publicity for the Department at the start of a weekend. "If it bleeds, it leads," he reminded his subordinates.

Bergdorf told Horstmeyer he thought that treatment harsh; Damon had enough bad things coming his way, why turn the Marcus murder into a circus? Horstmeyer laughed and said the Department needed some good news after the riots. Horstmeyer called one of the county's assistant prosecutors on the phone and told him what they had on Damon. The prosecutor concurred that was sufficient probable cause to issue an arrest warrant for Damon on rape and murder charges. Horstmeyer ordered Bergdorf and Nowakowski to head to Walnut Hills before school let out on Friday and arrest Damon there, with the full hands cuffed behind his back treatment.

In the face of that direct order, Bergdorf complied, sickened though he was. Nothing good would come of this treatment. By the time the detectives returned to District One with Damon in the back of the car, Horstmeyer already called a hasty news conference. Television cameras captured video of Damon being "perp walked" into the building, which the local TV stations aired on the six o'clock evening news. Horstmeyer told the assembled reporters, myself included, that detectives arrested a suspect in the Leah Marcus murder. He explained, while giving due credit to Bergdorf and Nowakowski specifically, that Leah's ex-boyfriend committed the crime and that the police had DNA evidence to support that accusation. He was relieved to be able to put the Marcus family at ease that Leah's killer had been found and to also alleviate the community's fear as a whole that a dangerous killer was no longer on the loose.

The video of Damon walking into police headquarters shows a young, black man, head bowed. When television reporters thrust microphones in his face, he neither looks at the camera nor responds to their queries. Damon later told me he thought it all a mistake. He knew he was innocent. He was ashamed that his friends and teachers would see these pictures. Mostly, he was mortified for the embarrassment it would cause his parents. He could handle the burden, he felt; but what would it do to his mother and father?

The Marcus family's nightmare had been going on for a month. The Allbright family's was just beginning.

Chapter Twenty

Though He Slay Me, Yet Will I Trust in

Him

—Job 13:15

       Long after his arrest, officers transported Damon to the Hamilton County Justice Center, the county jail, at 1000 Sycamore Street to await court processing. Horstmeyer knew that if Damon arrived there before midnight, he would hit the arraignment docket the next morning. But if he arrived at the jail after midnight, Damon would have to wait for his hearing until Tuesday. Let him stew. The justice center sat directly across the street from the Hamilton County Courthouse at 1000 Main Street. The two buildings shared an enclosed, overhead walkway that allowed prisoners to be securely walked into the courthouse from the jail.

       Damon never in his life had set foot in the justice center. None of his friends had criminal issues. He knew of young men from his father's church and the community of African American males as a whole who spent time there. He spoke occasionally with these men about their experiences with the criminal justice system. But his personal mind-set of the world could no more encompass what it would be like to spend a few nights in jail any more than he could imagine flying to the moon on a rocket ship.

The electronic buzzers and slamming of doors caught his attention. Jail officers searched him, issued him his requisite orange jumpsuit, and put him into the milieu of the population, most of who, like him, awaited court dates, be they arraignments or trials. Some person's fate had already been adjudicated, and they were spending their time in jail for offenses not serious enough to merit a trip to the penitentiary. Overcrowded was an understatement. Damon likened the environment to a beehive or an anthill; people were everywhere.

Despair and anxiety hit at the same time. He felt as though he were Daniel in the lion's den or perhaps Job in the belly of the whale. He figured that whichever metaphor best applied, this situation would make going to a state prison seem like a day on the beach. If he were to be convicted and sent to "the big house," he would probably feel more like an early Christian fed to the lions at the Coliseum.

Despite his initial dread, he soon found the mood in the jail population non-threatening, almost, he realized, a friendly place. He saw plenty of young men around his age or early twenties, black and white with an occasional Latino mixed in. People greeted old friends or made new ones. Inmates traded stories about what was happening on the outside, or what happened on their hearings, who the best and worst judges were, and all sorts of information pertaining to the criminal justice system.

Listening to the chatter, he learned that many of the people caught up in the net of the system were folks who violated drug laws, using or selling. "They got me for having a joint in my pants pocket after a traffic stop," he heard; or, "They found twenty marijuana plants in the basement of the house I was staying at. They weren't even mine; they belonged to my cousin." He heard the usual protestations of innocence.

No one hazed him. No one tried to stare him down or pick a fight with him. Several inmates came up to him just to engage in the usual banter. He was prepared, though. Isaiah prepared him.

When Bergdorf and Nowakowski arrested him at school that day, one of his friends called his mother. She called Isaiah Jones, and Jones left his office in a hurry to meet Damon at police headquarters. Jones gave Damon a brief lesson on life inside the jail, what it would be like, what to expect, and, most of all, what not to talk about. The one taboo subject for Damon during his incarceration concerned Leah Marcus. Jones impressed upon Damon the need for absolute silence regarding the charges. Jailhouse snitches would sell you down the river to the prosecutor in exchange for a better sentence or reduced charge. Even if Damon thought he said something totally innocent, it might be misconstrued and later used at trial, if the case actually went that far. (Jones later told me that he had no doubt the case would go to trial. Try as he would, the DNA evidence would be enough to keep the wheels of justice grinding forward.)

When people approached Damon and asked what he was in for, he shut the conversations down fast. One inmate laughed and said, "Well, ain't you the Fifth Amendment." The nickname stuck; throughout Damon's tenure in the justice center, he would henceforth be called "Fifth Amendment" or just "here comes the Fifth" for short.

Damon didn't know much about the criminal justice system yet, but he was glad that his parents hired Isaiah Jones. Delores and Othello discussed in detail what lawyer to hire for Damon. The moment Delores sensed that Bergdorf and Nowakowski circled Damon like sharks around a bleeding piece of bait, she knew the family had to hire Damon a good lawyer—the best lawyer. She knew her son did not kill Leah, but she had to make sure that he wasn't railroaded like so many African American suspects. She admitted to me the slightest doubt in her faith in her son's innocence after the police announced that Damon's DNA resided in Leah's body. Still, she told me, there had to be a reasonable explanation that still supported his innocence. In any event, when the detectives originally visited her and Damon, she held no doubt that Damon did not harm Leah.

She and Othello wanted the best attorney in town. They had several choices of excellent criminal defense lawyers. The deciding calculus she employed to make the determination with Othello revolved around the race of the lawyer. She admitted to me that that was cynical. Both

147

parents thought that, at the end of the day, no white lawyer would completely "get" Damon's conundrum, nor fight for him as aggressively as a lawyer of color, a person who grew up in the community and daily faced the racism and dismissiveness of whites. If the prosecutor ultimately filed charges against Damon for the murder of Leah, then Damon's very life, and at least a long stretch of his liberty, would be at stake. Isaiah Jones fit the bill; the Allbrights knew him well and knew him personally, as a friend to the black community and a man who had the smarts to stand up to the system, but do it in a way that was aggressive yet non-threatening to whites.

No one could predict what Damon's jury might look like. The odds of a predominantly African American jury would be slim given the demographics of Hamilton County, from which the jury pool would be chosen. Therefore, she acknowledged, a result like in the O. J. Simpson murder trial would not be in Damon's future. A mixed-race jury would not acquit Damon solely as payback for years of abuse of African Americans by the CPD. Delores had no compunction about calling a criminal a criminal. She held no doubt that Simpson murdered his ex-wife and the Goldman fellow who turned up to be at the wrong place at the wrong time. A lawyer like Jones would score points with people of color on the jury, and the white jurors would not be threatened by him. Many such juries had, in the past, been enthralled by Jones, whose summations sounded like oratory, a combination of Clarence Darrow and a Sunday preacher.

Damon would spend two and a half days in the justice center in relative anonymity. All that would change after his initial appearance on Tuesday, May 29.

Chapter Twenty-One

The Arraignment

Damon Allbright stood before a judge for his initial appearance, called an arraignment, at 9:00 a.m. on Tuesday morning. Sheriff's deputies herded him and thirty other arrestees downstairs, men and women, held in the justice center, to Room A and into the arraignment room of Municipal Court Judge Daniel Brown, who presided for the week. Arraignment court looked like a cattle call, and that's what the lawyers called it.

To the uninitiated, it looked scary, perfunctory, and yielded little hope that the arrested people would be getting out of jail any time soon. The purpose of the arraignment is to plead not guilty and, the thing most of these people were interested in, a discussion concerning the possibility of bail. The reality for most suspects charged with a serious felony does not entail being released on bail. The judge will set bail too high for them to be able to post it. Most will stay locked up for extended periods of time pending trial. If convicted, the pretrial detention will be credited towards the ultimate sentence. If the charges get dismissed, or you are acquitted, then you simply lost "X" number of days of your life that you will never get back.

Damon already knew that the police arrested him for the rape and murder of Leah. The proceeding held no mystery as to the charges or his rights, which Isaiah already explained to him. For Damon, it came down to two questions. Would he be released on a reasonable bail pending trial? Or would he rot in one of Dante's circles of hell? He couldn't quite figure out if it would be the first, Limbo; the second, Lust; or the seventh, Violence. He remembered reading *The Inferno* in his junior year for English class. Lust seemed reasonable, since the State would soon be charging him with rape. Violence also made sense since the State would also charge him with murder. But upon reflection, he thought Limbo made the most sense, because until he was tried, and either convicted or found not guilty, his life was stuck on hold, in a terrible state of neutral. Like that plane he thought about when the engine stopped in midair. Or a whitewater rafting trip on the New River in West Virginia he once took when the boat poised over the top of a small waterfall; he knew the bottom would drop out in a second, and he would either capsize and be thrown from the raft or continue in triumph down the river.

The judge took the cases of people who had engaged private counsel first. This little courtesy allowed private lawyers to get back to the business of making money sooner than public lawyers who had no such constraints concerning billable hours. The public defenders would go next, and the lowliest of suspects, those without a lawyer, went last.

Besides the multitudes of court personnel, arrestees in orange jump suits, lawyers, passersby who just stopped in to watch, a handful of law school students, and family members of the accused,[4] a number of reporters perched in locations guaranteed to give them a good view. The closer to the front the better, so they could hear whatever a soft-spoken defendant might say in response to the judge's questioning. I sat in the front row, having been following the case since the first reports of Leah's death.

My report of the proceeding would be short and factual. If I hurried back to the office, just a few blocks from the courthouse, my article would hit the afternoon presses. What I didn't expound on in my article were my impressions. My very first impression concerned Damon in a jumpsuit. He looked like any number of young men, black or white, in the requisite jailhouse uniform. The orange jumpsuit spits out the word 'guilty.' You can't spin away that stigma. When trial comes, judges allow defendants still housed in the justice center to wear street clothes lest the contamination of the jumpsuit sway jurors' minds.

As I watched Damon before the judge came in, I noticed he didn't banter or even

---

[4] My experience told me that few members of victims' families showed up at arraignments. However, Ben, Sarah, and David Marcus all attended. Ben and Sarah would show up at every single proceeding in Damon's case. Damon's parents also attended every court proceeding.

interact with his fellow inmates. He observed his surroundings making mental calculations of how all this would affect him. He didn't appear scared, but he looked like he didn't belong there. Tall, handsome, intelligent, he did not look the part of a murderer. I suppose neither did Ted Bundy, although Bundy's self-defense efforts (he represented himself in his criminal case in Florida) ultimately let the jurors see who he really was. He was convicted and electrocuted. Damon's parents also attended, as did their oldest child, Mary, the lawyer from Columbus. The Marcus family members kept a wary distance from the Allbright family.

A little after nine, the bailiff called the courtroom to order, the groundswell of talking muted, like a finger triggering a button on the TV remote control. Judge Daniel Brown entered the room and took his seat on the bench. Brown, a forty-eight-year-old man, held his position as judge for almost eight years. The governor appointed him to the bench mid-term of Brown's predecessor, who died in office. Two years later, Brown ran for election as the incumbent; although never elected himself, won, and had just been re-elected in the 2000 elections that, among other surprises, brought George W. Bush into the White House.

Brown is handsome, affable, and a career politician. Like most judges in Ohio, he came from the prosecutor's office. But he also came from a long line of politically connected Cincinnatians who held local and state office. The name "Brown" is one of the most recognized in

Ohio politics. Name recognition is half the battle for politicians.

A judge, a political creature, in Hamilton County, Ohio, is by definition a law and order man or woman. Fair, but firm. A public defender would find it nigh impossible to get elected to a judgeship. That said, these same judges, whose legal point of view steeped in a miasma of criminal mischief that would jade anyone's point of view after years of witnessing the affronts committed by people upon their family, neighbors, or strangers, would never admit on the record that they sided with the prosecution. But, most of the time, they did just that. The constraints on blatant cheerleading for the prosecution, nonetheless, were several. First, the individual ethos of these men and women reminded them daily of the need to be impartial. Second, as a group, judges, like most lawyers, are smart people; when they smell an injustice perpetrated on a citizen by the police or even their former colleagues, the prosecutors, they won't sit back and protect the establishment at the expense of the defendant. Third, trial judges know their decisions might be reviewed by a court of appeal. Trial judges hate to have their decisions overturned, so they try very hard to follow the law. They know, though, that they have a lot of discretion that won't be overturned by a reviewing court. Fourth, by necessity, they view every case through the lens of politics. Those optics may not change an outcome, but they will be weighed in the decision-making process.

Perhaps the best-known local example of this is when the then baseball commissioner, Bart Giamatti, banned Pete Rose for life from baseball. Rose was one of the Cincinnati Reds most storied players and still the Major League all-time hit king. Giamatti's investigator, John Dowd, started working the case, but Rose filed a suit in Hamilton County Common Pleas Court to gain an injunction to stall the matter. The judge assigned to the case granted the injunction. Major League Baseball subsequently had the case removed to federal court, where a judge allowed the matter to proceed. The common pleas judge assigned the case had slim legal grounds to issue an injunction; but failing to do so would have been political suicide in the city where Pete Rose grew up, played most of his career, and was beloved by thousands.

To get politics out of the courthouse, many states have laws that allow the governor or a commission of experts to appoint judges. This makes for (but doesn't really remove the element of politics completely) a less partisan affair in the selection of judges. By removing politics, judges can concentrate on handling the merits of the case. The US Constitution enshrines this core belief by allowing the president to nominate all Article Three judges (the Supreme Court, federal courts of appeal, and federal district courts). Subject to approval by the Senate, these judges serve for life, supposedly immune from politics.

Judge Brown, though, like all Ohio judges, is a political animal. The politics of Damon's case, which he would not handle at the trial stage, nonetheless played a minor role in the hearing that morning with respect to the decision about Damon's bail.

Damon watched with fascination how the judge handled bail for the four cases called before his. These four individuals all had various felonies of differing seriousness. The cases concerned felonious assault in the commission of an armed robbery, felony drug trafficking, a white-collar crime concerning an accountant who stole money from her employer, and an arson case. The judge ordered bail in all of the cases. The robber, the drug trafficker, and the arsonist (all alleged) had bail set in the tens or low hundreds of thousands of dollars. The white-collar criminal (alleged), a woman with no prior record and extensive ties to the community, had to post bail in the cash amount of the money that she (allegedly) stole, almost half a million dollars.

The bailiff called Damon's case next, and he stepped forward to the defense table where Isaiah Jones waited for him. Dan Brown knew Isaiah from dozens of cases the two had together, not to mention Jones's reputation and multiple bar-related activities. Jones made sure that the judge knew who Damon was. Damon had no criminal record other than two minor speeding tickets as a sixteen-year-old. Damon carried an almost straight "A" record at Walnut Hills where he excelled at sports and extracurricular activities. His father, the Reverend Othello Allbright (that was the politics code word that Jones dropped on Judge Brown); his mother, Delores; and his sister, a lawyer from Columbus, all came to court today to be at his side and support him. Damon held a leadership position in the Mt. Carmel Baptist Church youth group (again, code word that the Allbright faction could marshal voter turnout at the next election, far away as it might seem that day in May of 2001). Damon lived his entire life in Cincinnati, planned to go to the University of Cincinnati in the fall, and might end up on the very pulpit that his father currently held. (Politics yet again.)

The assistant prosecutor reminded the judge of the serious nature of the charges—rape and murder—with which the State had charged Damon. The matter had yet to be heard by a grand jury, but the possibility existed that Damon would be charged with a capital offense. Therefore, the judge should consider an increased potential for flight in the face of charges that could lead to the death penalty.

Brown no doubt felt politically boxed in. A low bail for a young man charged with such serious crimes, even a person with no prior record from a good family like Damon, would appear anathema to the law and order community in Hamilton County, particularly the white community. Yet, a high bail for a person unlikely to flee would penalize a man still innocent until proven guilty. By being locked away in jail, it would be that much harder for Damon and his defense team to handle the case. The purpose of bail, Brown knew, of course, was simply to ensure the appearance of the defendant at trial.

In a Solomon-like decision, Brown split the baby. He ordered bail at two million dollars.

Damon's jaw sagged. Isaiah would remind him that his family need only come up with ten percent in cash, $200 thousand. A large sum of money, but the Allbright family, the judge figured, could find a way if they could afford the services of Isaiah Jones.

Chapter Twenty-Two

Free Damon!

After all the defendants' arraignments were finished, the deputies escorted the thirty prisoners back upstairs to the detention portion of the justice center. Damon would sit there for some time unless and until his family could post bail. That afternoon, the entire milieu knew that Damon faced rape and murder charges, very serious felonies among a population of mostly minor infractors. Serious charges carried serious cachet in a jail. Other prisoners looked differently at Damon now. The quiet young man hid quite a wicked persona. Even though, as they all knew with a wink and a nod, Damon was innocent until proven guilty.

People wanted to talk to Damon now about his crime. Some of them just had curiosity animating them, trying to find out the story. Others probably wanted to play jailhouse snitch, as Isaiah Jones warned Damon some would do. Damon strictly enforced the "no talking about the case" rule Isaiah laid down. He heard "Fifth Amendment" a lot the rest of that Tuesday.

Damon pondered how his family could possibly come up with $200 thousand to post bail. He knew that his parents already agreed to pay Isaiah $50 thousand, which constituted a large portion of their savings. The thought of wasting in jail for months before a trial, maybe even a year, if, God forbid, as Jones told him, the prosecutor asked for death penalty specifications, weighed heavily on Damon's consciousness.

While Damon whiled away his time in the justice center, Othello and Delores consulted with Jones about how to come up with the bail. Jones explained they had three options. They could post the ten percent bond in cash, which the court would return to them provided Damon appeared at all proceedings. They could post property, say their house, if they had sufficient equity in it after their mortgage, to cover the bond. A lien would be placed on the home but released, provided, again, that Damon appeared at all hearings. Third, they could pay ten percent of the ten percent, $20 thousand, to a bail bondsman. They would never get that money back, though; that was how bondsmen made their living.

The Allbrights had a few dollars left in their accounts after paying Jones and a little equity in the home. But they did not have the ability to cover option one or two. They despised option three because they saw no sense in forfeiting money to a bondsman when Damon would be sure to appear anyway. Even though the police said they found his DNA in Leah's body, Damon must have a viable explanation that supported his innocence. He would show at trial to prove his innocence. Isaiah reminded them that Damon had nothing to prove. The burden of proof, beyond a reasonable doubt, rested on the State of Ohio.

Returning to work that afternoon, Othello spoke with his associate pastor, Herbert Wilkinson, IV. Herbert, a thirty-five-year-old man with a quieter, more cerebral demeanor than Othello, came from a long line of preachers, stretching back four generations. The differences in their personalities made for an excellent team. Between the two of them, they managed to appeal to just about every member of the flock. Herb suggested that the church loan Othello the money, but Othello flatly refused. Those funds were earmarked for charitable purposes and to maintain the church facilities. No way would he use those funds for personal aggrandizement.

Herb acknowledged Othello's righteousness but said he would not be satisfied with leaving Damon to rot in jail. He assured Othello he would work on a solution.

The riots ended six weeks before, but their memory loomed large in Cincinnati's collective consciousness. People within and without the community began to react and call for change. Pressure from outside began when celebrities indicated they would boycott appearances in the city. Smokey Robinson, Whoopi Goldberg, Wynton Marsalis, and Bill Cosby (before he found himself the subject of derision and faced criminal charges himself) all cancelled upcoming appearances. The Urban League cancelled its annual convention scheduled to be in town that year. Locally, black leaders called for a boycott of Cincinnati businesses.

These ideas percolated in Herb's brain for a few days. After cogitating, and praying, about the matter, he told me that he was struck with an idea which he believed God gave to him in a dream. The community would take up a collection for Damon's bail money. It would be like passing around the collection plate at church, except on a city-wide basis. He would contact the other African American ministers, many of whom he and Othello knew personally, of course. They would assist. The outrage of the community would galvanize citizen involvement. Except, he told Othello, these would not be anonymous donations. People would be given receipts for their ten or twenty dollars. After Damon got his bail money back, all the supporters would be reimbursed in full. Othello loved the idea. It was, he told me years later, like a precursor to a GoFundMe page in the pre-digital age.

For weeks, pastors brought the issue up in their churches. Local black press ran free advertisements seeking donations. Collection boxes sprang up at the churches manned by volunteers who gave each donor a handwritten receipt. Black radio stations promoted the issue. In shades of the O. J. Simpson case, "Free Damon!" banners hung over highway overpasses. Other people spray-painted the slogan on overpasses, underpasses, or building walls. Local press, TV, radio, and print, including my paper, ran stories on the "Free Damon!" phenomenon.

In an overwhelming triumph of community cohesiveness, Herb's "Army for

Damon" collected funds to cover Damon's bail in a little over four weeks. Othello and Delores marched into the clerk of court office at the courthouse on Friday, June 29, and posted a cashier's check to secure Damon's release.

The family reunited on the ground floor of the justice center later that afternoon. Tears streaked Delores's face. The family hugged and prayed together on the concourse of the facility. But while Damon sat in jail for a little over a month, his case did not sit derailed. It kept chugging down the line of the criminal justice system like a locomotive on greased rails.

Chapter Twenty-Three

Grand Jury

Probable cause to believe a crime was committed is often the starting point for a suspect's involvement in the criminal justice system. The police witness a crime and so have probable cause to believe the suspect committed it. Or they investigate a crime after the fact and find reason to believe a person committed a crime. A prosecutor then reviews this decision before a felony arrest in the case of a crime not committed in the presence of the police. But the process doesn't stop there in Hamilton County. Oversight by the court system or the citizenry occurs next. Before the mid-1990s, the court held a preliminary hearing to determine if probable cause existed. Defense attorneys liked this system, as it afforded them an early view of the strengths of the prosecution's case. But that changed when the county switched to the grand jury indictment system.

In the American criminal justice system, two kinds of juries operate. The petit (small) jury hears criminal cases and makes determinations of guilt or no guilt. Typically, twelve citizens serve on felony juries. But a grand jury is a larger group of citizens gathered in secret by the prosecutor. These juries can contain up to twenty-six members. In Hamilton County, eleven citizens serve for a two-week stint. Nine jurors vote, but there are two extras in case somebody would happen to know one of the accused. A minimum of seven members must vote in favor of an indictment, which is a determination by the panel that probable cause exists to try an individual for a crime. Ostensibly, this serves as a citizen oversight of prosecutorial power. As a practical matter, since the proceeding is secret and only the prosecutor, the jury, and any witnesses—typically, the investigating police officer—are present, the jury hears a one-dimensional side of the case and usually rubber-stamps what the prosecutor wants.

Marilyn Cho ran the grand jury panel in the month of June, and that was the next stop of Damon's case along the path to trial. Cho graduated from the University of Cincinnati College of Law, interned with prosecutor's office, and landed a job with them after graduation. She ran grand juries for several years at that point and had down pat the mechanics of get in, get out of the room in a hurry. Typically, a presentation would last about a half hour. She would leave the room, then the jury would vote. That took about two minutes. They would hit a buzzer to tell her they had reached a verdict, which almost always was in favor of indicting a suspect.

She brought Simon Bergdorf before the panel on Tuesday, June 12. He explained the investigation of Leah's death, culminating with the DNA match between Damon's buccal swab and the semen found in Leah's body. Based on that information, the jury issued an indictment on two counts.

The first count alleged a violation of rape under Ohio Revised Code §2907.02(A)(2), which provides that, "No person shall engage in sexual conduct with another when the offender purposely compels the other to submit by force or threat of force." The second count alleged a violation of aggravated murder under Revised Code §2903.01(B), which provides that, "No person shall purposely cause the death of another...while committing or attempting to commit...rape..."

A charge of aggravated murder can result in death penalty specifications, but such a determination must come from the members of the grand jury. The prosecutor can ask for it, but the jury must decide. If they fail to make death penalty specifications in the indictment, the defendant will only face a penalty of up to life in prison without parole.

Cho had enough experience under her belt to seek counsel with other members of her office, including the elected prosecuting attorney (politics, again!) and Matt Lehane, the county's head of the criminal division, who tried virtually all the murder cases for Hamilton County. Before she asked the grand jury for death penalty specs, she wanted to make sure the top boss approved of the idea (he did not, given the politics of the case and the youth, good name, and lack of record of the defendant) and if Lehane could even make such a charge stick (he did not believe so based on the evidence so far).

I interviewed Lehane for this book in 2012. He did not begin his career in law. He served in the army, then became a high school teacher at one of Cincinnati's Catholic boys' high schools. During his tenure there, he decided to become a lawyer, and enrolled in the night law school program at the Salmon P. Chase College of Law at Northern Kentucky University. Then he joined the prosecutor's office, where, soon, he became the go-to prosecutor for murder cases. In 2001, he already tried over 150 murder cases, most to conviction. He had a sixth sense about a case from its earliest stages. The homicide detectives often consulted him even before bringing charges against a suspect. They respected Lehane's judgment. If Lehane said it would stick, it probably would.

From Lehane's earliest involvement in the Allbright case, that sixth sense troubled him with regard to going for a death penalty specification. That issue had nothing to do with the political optics; that was for his boss, the county prosecutor, to call that shot. From a trial strategy perspective, he didn't have a good enough feel that he could make the rape stick. If the rape fell, then the murder charge would too. All this would play out, as he predicted, at Damon's trial.

Based on the prosecutor's political call, and Lehane's practical trial experience call, Cho did not push for death penalty specifications, and the grand jury did not issue any with the indictment. The indictment was duly filed with the clerk of the court. The prosecuting attorney made sure to call a press conference to announce the indictment that afternoon, the twelfth of

June. As a courtesy, Cho telephoned Jones to advise him what had happened.

Jones walked over to the justice center to tell Damon the not unexpected news. The case would proceed. Trial preparation would start in earnest.

Chapter Twenty-Four

Judge Frederick Burger

On Wednesday, June 13, following the indictment, the clerk's office randomly assigned Damon's case to a judge literally by a roll of the dice. Sixteen judges sit on the bench. In 2001, all were men except for one African American woman, who was also the only judge of color. The odds dictated that a white male would handle Damon's case. The random roll went to the docket of Frederick Burger, a fifty-six-year-old judge, who started his career on the bench in the municipal court (that handled minor civil cases and misdemeanor criminal cases) at age thirty-seven before ascending to the common pleas court two election cycles later at the age of fifty. Like many politicians and judges, he affiliated with the Republican Party in this county. Like Matt Lehane, Burger came up through the prosecutor's office and even mentored Lehane at the beginning of his career. Like Lehane, he was a Catholic, although of German, not Irish descent, with a strong affiliation with local parochial schools. He went to college at Xavier University and law school at Notre Dame.

Lawyers who practiced criminal cases before Burger knew him as a no-nonsense, let's move the case along kind of judge. He didn't like jury trials, because they clogged up his court. But once he had a jury trial, he presided with charm, because every potential juror, every seated juror, every witness, and every family member or friend who came to the trial was a prospective voter. He also liked publicity. Following the grand jury indictment, the defendant will appear again in court for another arraignment. Often the trial judge delegates this perfunctory hearing to a magistrate. Burger would not miss the opportunity to have this hearing in his own courtroom before TV cameras. Oh, the publicity!

Deputies escorted Damon down from the justice center again on Friday, June 15, for his arraignment hearing. Isaiah Jones met with Damon the day before to talk about the process. Isaiah would press for a reduction in bail, knowing that Damon's supporters collected a large amount of funds already for the "Free Damon!" fund. A reduction, though, would help everyone and allow Damon to be released even sooner.

Ben and Sarah Marcus sat behind the prosecutor's table, but Lehane did not sit at that desk. A more junior assistant handled the arraignment docket. I sat in the front row behind the defense table. TV cameras recorded the action. Burger, looking judicial, offered to have the indictment read in open court. Jones declined; he had already seen it. Burger re-advised Damon of his rights and then proceeded to re-hear the issue of bail. The prosecutor seemed satisfied with a $2 million bail.

Isaiah Jones rose from his seat and reiterated for the judge, and the TV cameras, for all those blacks who might vote for this judge at his next election, that Damon had no prior record, earned a 3.7 GPA at the best public high school in the state, and would be attending a local university in the fall. He went through Damon's academic, athletic, extracurricular, and church activities. He noted Damon's good family and spelled out the Mt. Carmel Baptist Church by name, lest Burger have any confusion as to what family Damon Allbright belonged to.

The assistant prosecutor reminded the judge of the heinous allegations that the indictment spelled out. She reminded the judge that the Allbright home sat just a few blocks from the Marcus home, and the Marcuses might feel threatened if Damon were released on bond and allowed to live in his house again.

Jones told me that before she made that comment, he was sure Burger would leave bond as is. But that comment struck Burger as a reverse "race card" issue, to which he likely took offense. He lowered bail to $1.5 million. Damon exhaled, as did his parents; they were well on their way to amassing $150 thousand. Sarah Marcus grabbed Ben's arm, nails digging in so hard that even through his suit coat and dress shirt, her nails left marks on his appendage.

The judge had no idea, although he had seen the media coverage, whether the Allbright campaign to "Free Damon!" had any real hope of springing Damon from jail. Burger did know that

171

speedy trial rules in Ohio required him to hold a trial for Damon within ninety days of his arrest if Damon remained incarcerated that entire time. The police arrested Damon on Friday, May 25. Ninety days meant the trial had to start on or before Thursday, August 23. (Speedy trial dates could be waived by the defense; also, the time could be tolled for various technicalities. For defendants out on bail, the statute required a trial date in 270, not 90 days.) But, for now, Burger had to set a trial before the end of August.

To accommodate that timetable, he needed to allow time for the parties to engage in discovery and to hold a pretrial hearing, where the parties fight over various motions integral to the case before the case ever heads to trial. Burger ordered discovery to take place during the next forty-five days. He allowed this expanded discovery timetable given the high stakes nature of the case and the scientific evidence that the parties might introduce at trial. He set the pretrial for Monday, July 30, as forty-five days fell on the course of a weekend day. At that hearing, he would set a formal trial date, but he already instructed his staff to clear the week of August 20 for a trial.

Lehane heard about all of this from his colleague at lunch that afternoon. Secretly, he liked that the roll of the dice led to Burger's courtroom. For that very same reason, Jones disliked his luck on that roll. Lawyers who practiced before Burger called him (behind his back) a nickname.

They called him "The Hammer."

Chapter Twenty-Five

Discovery

The county prosecutor assigned Matt Lehane as trial counsel for the case of *State v. Allbright*. Lehane expected that. He tried the most murder cases in the office. Lehane knew Isaiah Jones well, having worked on six murder cases with him over the years. Lehane liked and respected Jones and knew they would work well together, even if there might be minor clashes of aggressiveness and grandstanding. The tough part of working a jury case with Jones was the difference in their courtroom personalities. While Jones could be a tad bombastic in front of a jury, usually he came across as a committed and righteous defender of a defendant's rights. This attitude sometimes resonated with jurors, even the typical law and order type of juries back in those days. Most juries then consisted of ten or eleven white people and only one or two African Americans. In any case, Lehane's style was less dramatic, more factual and logical. He told juries that their decisions must be premised on the facts and the law, not the heartstring tug of their emotions.

The Rules of Criminal Procedure permit a defendant to have access to the State's evidence.

Lehane collected all the material that Bergdorf and Nowakowski amassed during the investigation (except for Bergdorf's index cards, which even Lehane had neither knowledge of nor access to) and collated them into three large binders, which he had a courier walk down the street to Jones's office.

Before he did this, though, he spent a considerable amount of time reviewing it himself, looking for holes in the case that someone like Jones might be expected to exploit. The binders contained so much information, starting with a transcript of Sarah Marcus's 9-1-1 call through Damon's arrest and processing, Miranda Noble's report, the EMT/fire department logs, Bergdorf's and Nowakowski's notes, the crime scene photos, the criminalist's notes, Sergeant McDaniel's report, the interview of Alice Bowman, the autopsy report; the fingerprint, hair, and DNA analyses; interviews with witnesses, the videotaped interview of Vernon Banks, and more, all were included in these binders.

On its face, the case appeared solid; solid enough that had Damon's lawyer been a public defender, Lehane would call him or her in a week and offer to start discussions about a plea bargain. But Lehane told me that, even without the potential holes in the case that he already identified, a defendant like Damon Allbright, from that family, with those credentials, and having a lawyer like Jones, was not likely to want to plead out. He would take his chances with a trial and run the risk of getting a long sentence by Fred "the Hammer" Burger if he were convicted.

The courier delivered the package to Jones's office, on 9ᵗʰ Street, just a few blocks from the courthouse, on Friday, June 15. Jones cancelled his appointments for that day and studied the file in detail, taking copious notes and cogitating about things. Now he learned most of what Lehane knew. What Jones didn't know yet was, "What does Damon know?" Jones held one advantage over Lehane. Jones would soon learn what Damon did know and would use that to his advantage in preparing his defense. Isaiah spent the rest of the day and evening thinking about the case and making arrangements to visit Damon in the justice center the next morning, on Saturday.

The State had no real witnesses to the crime. While eyewitness testimony is inherently unreliable, he wouldn't even have to go down that road. The State had no statement from Damon, least of all a confession. The prosecution had no jailhouse snitch willing to offer up Damon's incriminating in-jail statement; so far, Isaiah's admonition to Damon to stay quiet in the justice center worked like a charm.

The prosecution would rely on forensic evidence. The crime lab report held the sixteen-inch battleship shell that Lehane planned to explode and, thereby, plaster Damon all over the courtroom with. When Lehane was finished presenting that evidence, with talk of zillions to one that only Damon could be the man whose semen filled Leah's body, the jury would be ready to hang him. On its face, that evidence presented massive problems for Jones. Unlike the O. J. Simpson case, he had no grounds to even argue that the police planted the evidence or contaminated the crime scene. No, 'bulletproof' best described the DNA match. He had to find a way around how Damon's semen got into Leah's body. Jones's agile mind framed a scenario where he might counter the DNA; but that plan hinged on what Damon would tell him when he interviewed him later.

The best bet to counter some of the forensics concerned Sarah Marcus covering Leah's dead body with a comforter. He would have to explore that in more detail with Damon. But the weight of the hair evidence paled in comparison to the damning nature of the semen.

Then there was the matter of whose DNA was that under Leah's fingernails? It wasn't Damon's. (He had already asked Damon about any marks on his body when they were together at the Homicide bureau offices.) This helps, Isaiah knew, somehow. He just had to find a way to make it fit a believable story.

The criminalists found Damon's fingerprint evidence all over the Marcus home, certainly in the bedroom. No doubt Leah and Damon had spent many hours together at home and in her bedroom. Prints from over the course of a two-year relationship proved nothing. Jones did not intend to deny that Damon had never been in the home. In fact, such evidence helped Damon more than hurt him, because those prior visits established that he had left his prints long before someone else came along and killed Leah. The prosecution could never prove *when* Damon left his prints in her room. Presumably, Damon and Leah had intercourse before April 12 and had done so in Leah's bedroom. Hence, the police found his hair and pubic hair on her bed, on the comforter, and on her body. The hairs could have been deposited from any of those prior sexual encounters, even if it was only one encounter prior to the date of Leah's death.

Jones found two potential bright spots in the discovery binders. One involved the mystery woman with a possible mystery passenger, identified by Alice Bowman, and the other involved Vernon Banks.

A classic defense strategy to gain an acquittal works something like this. "We don't have to prove that the defendant is innocent. It is the State's job to prove that he is guilty. They have to prove that beyond a reasonable doubt. If you find that there is sufficient doubt that the defendant didn't commit the crime, you must acquit him. Here, there are possibilities, reasonable possibilities, that someone other than the defendant killed Leah Marcus. There is the mystery woman with the mystery man in the car. And there is this four-time convicted child sex offender and pedophile who lives three doors down the street and whose fingerprints were found on Leah's piano room window by the very police who investigated the murder."

If Damon had an alibi for his whereabouts on the afternoon of April 12, that could be most helpful. Nonetheless, alibi defenses prove difficult sometimes. They have to be as bulletproof as the State's forensic evidence. Otherwise, a crafty prosecutor can rip the defense to shreds. The question of alibi, by necessity, would have to wait until Isaiah interviewed Damon.

On Saturday, Isaiah trundled a large, wheeled briefcase with the discovery materials down to the justice center. He also had multiple notepads and pens to take notes. He explained to Damon, again, that their conversations were privileged. Nothing Damon said to him could ever be repeated to anyone without Damon's express consent. Therefore, to assist Damon to the fullest, Damon needed to be absolutely honest with Jones, so, together, they could come up with the best possible defense.

One question defense attorneys never ask their clients goes like this: "Did you commit the crime?" If the defendant answers in the affirmative, the attorney has an ethical bind about how to manage a defense case when he or she knows the client is guilty.

True to form, when I interviewed Jones years later, he refused to talk about the confidential client discussions he held with Damon. He had no problem discussing aspects of the case that remained part of the public record.

Damon, however, shared with me the details of that, and other, jailhouse visits after the trial. He wanted the whole story on the record, in all its sordidness and pathos.

Chapter Twenty-Six

Confessions of a...Boyfriend

Ten years after Damon's trial, the *Tribune*
laid me off. The *Enquirer* put a dagger in the
Tribune's heart, finally killing off its old rival.
Print newspapers disappeared all over the
country, washed away in a digitized storm of
news served up electronically. Those papers that
survived turned to an online model as well as
subscription services. I tried to score a job with
the hated rival, but they didn't need another
crime reporter. They didn't need me in any
reporting capacity; they could barely afford to
keep their own staff and laid numbers of their
own off.

I turned to freelance work and eked out a
living, one of the leading edge of the gig economy
people, I suppose. Ends met; I kept my modest
house. There, I could sit on my front porch
overlooking the slope down to the street and
watch traffic buzz by as I sipped my cup of tea,
while balancing a tablet on my lap drafting some
article as a contributing writer to any of a
number of magazines. But with no office to
report to or facetime with a boss, I enjoyed a
newfound freedom to do what I want and write
what interested me. At the ten-year mark, I

realized that the Leah Marcus case had never let go of its hold over me, and I started looking into the events of that incendiary spring in 2001. I conducted many of the interviews for this book starting in late 2011. By 2013, I contacted Damon, and he agreed to be interviewed. He didn't recognize me from all the legal proceedings I attended during his case. He looked different to me, as well. He was a "grown-ass" man, he told me; he had filled out, his frame no longer that of a greyhound but not quite mastiff, either.

He no longer looked the carefree teen of his last Walnut Hills High School *Remembrancer* picture. His visage projected a sort of Zen acceptance of the world and his position in it. Damon had gone on to earn a college degree, a combined major of history and comparative religion. He then pursued a Master's in Divinity.

When we met, he came more alive than his recent photographs that he sent me suggested was his current frame of mind. He wanted to tell his story, wanted the world to know.

Damon exhibits a keen memory of events surrounding that summer. This seems counterintuitive given the passage of time. But in my journalistic travels and research, I learned that two parts of the brain coordinate the retention of long-term memories. When people suffer a trauma, the amygdala imprints a strong emotional response, usually of fear. Given that strong emotion, the amygdala deposits those thoughts into the hippocampus, the little sea-horsed shaped part of the brain that retains memory for the long haul. When traumas occur to young people, before they have their fully adult and mature brain (about age thirty), which might otherwise be able to process the problem and respond differently, the amygdala and hippocampus go into high gear. Never forgetting something fearful protects us from falling into the same trap again at some later date. Unfortunately, it also leads to PTSD. Therefore, I give credence to Damon's memories.[5]

He recalls the day, Saturday, June 16, when Isaiah Jones came to the justice center and spent several hours going over the case for the first time in detail.

"Thank you for coming, Mr. Jones. I know you are busy, and I appreciate you coming down on your day off to see me." Jones assured him that he rarely had a day off, especially with a big trial pending. "I also want to tell you that I will repay your fee in full after this is over. There's no way my parents should have to shoulder that burden. They've got younger kids they have to support, get to college. They have their retirement to worry about." Jones told him not worry about the money. And in case Damon wondered whether that *he* who paid the bill had access to the information, Jones reminded Damon that *Damon* was the client and anything

---

[5] The same process played out extensively with the #MeToo movement. People wanted to pillory victims for coming forward years after events occurred and claim, how could they remember? Even Supreme Court nominees fell into this morass.

he told Jones was privileged, even from his own parents who paid the lawyer fees. Should Damon choose to discuss the case with his parents, that was his choice; but the privilege would be waived, and arguably, the prosecutor could call his parents as hostile witnesses against Damon's interest in a trial.

With those boundaries spelled out, Damon told Isaiah the story of his dead girlfriend, Leah Marcus. Damon and Leah grew up just a few blocks away from each other. But those few blocks lay separated by a major highway artery, Reading Road, a four-lane, north-south road through the city running all the way up to Lake Erie as part of US Route 42. Little kids didn't cross Reading Road on their own without parental supervision. Even though they would have gone to primary school together, Leah's parents sent her to private school through the sixth grade. So the two young people never met, never even laid eyes on each other, until they both started school as seventh graders at Walnut Hills. "She was this tiny little girl in braces. Her breasts hadn't even started developing. As best as I could tell," he told me with a wan smile. "I mean, I saw her in the halls and stuff, but I ignored her. She wasn't cute back then. Plus, she was white. And I was black."

But then they met for real in eighth grade music class. Leah started to develop physically by then, and so Damon, like many a teenage boy, took notice of her, first as an object of lust. Then he heard her play her piano pieces, pieces that seemed so complicated no fourteen-year-old should have any business knowing how to play them. Listening to her was magic. Everyone knew, certainly I did, he told me, that she was a prodigy. "I told her she was going to grow up to be a famous concert pianist, a soloist, make a ton of records, win a lot of Grammys, and earn a mountain of cash." Except she didn't play like a diva. She didn't have those rolling body movements, the ballet lifts of the arms and hands off the keyboard, the shaking of the tresses of her hair.

"She sat stock still in front of that piano, but man, her hands, her hands, they just flew over those keys. She reminded me of old video I saw of the late great blind jazz pianist Art Tatum from back in the '40s and '50s. He would sit totally still without moving, but your eyes could not keep up with how fast his fingers moved over the keys. The big difference between their styles was Art played, unlike most piano players, flat-fingered, whereas most pianists bend the tips of their fingers and play with the hands arched. I guess that is how Art managed to look like his fingers moved at the speed of light. Or maybe the speed of sound." Damon laughed at his own pun.

By ninth grade, Leah accompanied Damon when he sang, and they presented many pieces together in all kinds of performances. She had also, by then, developed a curvier form, and Damon keenly noted the changes. "By tenth grade, I think I was falling in love with her. But how could I express that to her? I mean, she had filled out her clothes mighty fine, and she was hot. But she was also this sweet and nice and smart and caring person. Me, I was just a popular jock with a good singing voice. I didn't have the musical calling. I could never be the Robert to her Clara Schumann." Damon impressed me with his knowledge of Classical music with that allusion. "Besides, she was white, and I was black. I didn't know how that whole interracial thing might work out. Not only that, but I knew her family was super wealthy. Her dad, he was like the country's richest trial lawyer. And on top of all of that, she was Jewish and I'm Baptist, the son of a minister, and her mom's the daughter of a rabbi. Man, where could you have less in common between two people who might go out on a date?"

Damon mustered the courage to ask her out at the end of sophomore year, and they went on their first date. It was sweet and charming and exciting, but while Leah was a virgin, Damon wasn't. He had had sex with a couple of other girls before. Sure, he knew his parents probably would have frowned on the whole thing, but they were realistic as well as religious. "Young people were going to do it, and they knew it," was how he put it. Leah was okay with oral sex at first, but they finally had intercourse midway through their junior year. It wasn't even that hard to find space, a common enough problem for teenagers. The Marcus parents hardly ever spent time at home. Mr. Marcus was almost always working cases, late at night or out of town. Mrs. Marcus ran a company, too, and spent lots of hours at work, board meetings, and fundraising events. So the two kids had that big house on Burton Woods Lane all to themselves after Leah's older brother, David, went off to college, when Leah and Damon settled into their junior year at high school. They made good use of that house, all its nooks and crannies, not just Leah's bedroom. Leah's bedroom, her bed, the chaise lounge, the Oriental rug at the foot of the bed, they all witnessed in silence the scenes of amorous trysts over the months. The piano bench held a favorite place in their hearts, but the landing on the main staircase overlooking the front hall, her father's desk in the study, and others, all became accoutrements in their budding sex lives. I wondered, listening to Damon's story, whether that was why the police found Vernon Banks's fingerprints on the window sill of the piano room in the Marcus house. Did he watch her play the piano, or did he watch Damon play Leah on the bench?

Isaiah Jones did not have a prurient interest in Damon and Leah's sex life. He had a defense to build. He had many questions, questions that most of us would find uncomfortable talking about with a trusted friend, no less a stranger. The thought of airing such discussions out in front of a jury made Damon cringe. But Isaiah assured him, they had to talk about it now.

Isaiah wanted to know, did Damon or Leah engage in or like rough sex? Did he like to tie her up, or did she ever ask for that? Did they fight? How did they fight? Verbally? Physically? Did they communicate by cell phone? Text or talk? Mostly talk; text was too cumbersome on those flip phones. Isaiah would get a log of the calls and transcripts of the texts from Cincinnati Bell.

Did Damon cheat on Leah with another girl while he dated Leah? No, Damon assured him. Did she cheat on him? No, Damon assured him.

Two things Damon refused to discuss at that time with Isaiah, which must have troubled Isaiah. Did Damon and Leah engage in anal sex? And where was Damon on the afternoon of Thursday, April 12?

Chapter Twenty-Seven

Pretrial Lies

Isaiah Jones loves complex criminal trials. He likens them to chess matches and playing against a skilled opponent like Matt Lehane, that really got Jones's game on. Certainly, the most damning evidence the State had against Damon consisted of his DNA found in Leah's body. If he could swat that away, the case fell apart. In reviewing the discovery, he saw that the crime lab took many weeks to analyze the DNA evidence and make its report. He knew the county crime lab could run that in two weeks, maybe less, in an important case like this—especially, if pressed by both the CPD and the prosecutor's office. He didn't then know the innocent explanation that Dr. Patel vacationed in India and was not available to run the tests. Was there any monkey business involved here?

That turned out to be a dead end, but he considered getting an independent expert to analyze the DNA. He could file a motion and ask the court to pay for that, claiming Damon could no longer afford further expenses in his own defense. Doing so would be a gamble, a chess feint, he explained. If he got an independent expert that confirmed the crime lab's results, that would not help Damon. But here was where Jones showed what a master chess player he is. He likened it to the strategy of a sham queen sacrifice. If he failed to ask for an expert and Damon were later convicted, then Damon could argue on appeal that he had the ineffective assistance of counsel. Jones would sacrifice his own good name to help Damon build a winnable appeal.

Discovery is a two-way street. Damon had to turn over whatever he had to the prosecutor. But Damon had nothing. Jones hired no experts and probably would not do so.

Pretrial motions often include motions to suppress evidence and questions of competency of the defendant to stand trial. No question, Damon had the requisite competency; no motion for competency would yield any tangible result. Typical motions to suppress concern evidence seized by the police improperly or statements made by the defendant without adequate warning of his Miranda rights, his right to remain silent under the Constitution.

Following Damon's arrest, Bergdorf got a search warrant to look at Damon's house. The search yielded no evidence that the police found useful and that was duly noted in Bergdorf's notes.

Damon made only one relevant statement to Bergdorf about the case. Damon told the investigator on Friday, April 13, when the two detectives showed up at Damon's house, that he, Damon, had not seen Leah since the Saturday before her death. When Jones met with Damon in jail on June 16, Damon had not offered any explanation as to his whereabouts between Saturday and the Thursday when someone killed Leah. Therefore, Damon's statement to the police could hurt him. If Damon had, in fact, been with Leah after Saturday, and he took the stand and said so, the prosecutor would impeach him, that is make him out to be a liar, based on his prior statement. The devil was in the details, and Jones didn't have those details yet. *If* Damon really never saw Leah after Saturday, how possibly could his DNA end up in her body absent a colossal screw-up on the part of the crime lab? Jones saw little doubt but that Damon would have to take the stand. Jones needed a viable story of how and when Damon knew Leah (in the Biblical sense) after Saturday but before Thursday. Without an explanation, as to his side of the story, the jury would convict Damon based on the evidence.

Jones would probably have to file a motion to suppress that statement, with or without Damon's story of the events after Saturday. Jones did, in fact, file such a motion, which Burger later denied. Lehane skewered Damon with that statement at trial.

Damon said that Jones met with him again in jail on Wednesday, June 20. Jones again wanted Damon to tell him when Damon last saw Leah. Jones wanted an alibi, if Damon had one, for April 12.

According to Damon, Jones again reminded Damon that they needed an explanation for how his semen ended up in Leah's body. Perhaps Jones played a little loose with ethics here, or perhaps not. But he told

Damon (per Damon's account) that scientific evidence would support a scenario that had Damon and Leah engaged in sex acts up to twenty-four hours before her death, the semen would still be in her body—even if he never had sex with her again, specifically the next day, the day of the murder. I asked Jones about that conversation, which he declined to discuss— while looking uncomfortable—on the grounds of attorney-client privilege. I am not implying that Jones told Damon to do something untruthful. I don't even have Jones's side of the story to juxtapose against Damon's version of the tale. Nor am I willing to "convict" Jones on that charge, any more than Bergdorf was willing to "convict" Damon early on in the investigation when he exchanged a knowing glance with his mother.

But I will tell you this. Damon has a 130 IQ, even though science demonstrates that African Americans score lower on IQ tests than whites due to intrinsic racial bias in the questions. He had a 3.7 GPA at one of the best schools in the land. Damon is a smart fellow, and he read the invisible ink handwriting Jones (allegedly) left for him. If Damon testified that had he and Leah had sex on Wednesday, April 11, that testimony would undermine the DNA evidence. Yes, it was his DNA; but not from the day of the murder. Someone else killed her. If someone else raped her, they used a condom; maybe she wasn't raped at all on the twelfth. It didn't matter. The prosecution case rose and fell with the rape charge. If that falls away, so does the murder charge.

Damon, though, had an ethical problem of his own. His parents raised him to tell the truth, even uncomfortable truths. The consequences of truth-telling might be brutal, but they paled in comparison with the stain left on your soul by virtue of telling a lie.

Chapter Twenty-Eight

Other Lies

I interviewed Delores Allbright twice while researching this book. The second time, I called on her after I spoke with Damon in 2013. His interview caused me to have nagging concerns that I felt she might be able to shed light on.

Delores Allbright is a proud woman. A devout woman. She is the daughter of a preacher. She married a preacher. A righteous woman, she lives her life to honor God's glory and thoughts of the hereafter never stray far from her mind. But she does not live in a bubble. She is an activist, a community organizer, a loving mother to six children, and wife to her childhood sweetheart. She, like Othello, is realistic but optimistic. A joke she told me once, and one I never thought I would hear escape the lips of a preacher's daughter and wife, made me laugh.

One Sunday, during services, Preacher Willis calls on the choir up in the balcony to sing a hymn. He invites the flock to stand and join in. They all do so. The harmonious voices fill the chapel. The preacher closes his eyes, basking in the sounds of the voices and the organ, and when he opens them again his jaw drops. Up in the balcony, a beautiful twenty-year-old female choir member has shucked off her robe and stands stark naked, head uplifted to heaven, singing away. "Quick!" he shouts to the assembled. "No one dare turn around now, or God will surely strike you blind!" One old codger in the third row thinks to himself, as he closes one eye and turns to peer behind him, "It might be worth one eye!"

The sacred and the profane fill the earth, Delores knows, and there is no escaping the devil's meddling in the affairs of men and women. That doesn't mean we humans ignore our frailties; we strive to live life the way we know God wants us to. Mendacity, surely, she told me, could be added to the list and become the eighth deadly sin.

She came to learn that Damon lied about Leah. By the end of the trial, she knew for a fact that somewhere along the timeline of what he told her when Bergdorf showed up at the house and what he testified about on the stand, the truth lay run over in the street, the victim once again of human frailty and devilish trickeries.

Render unto Caesar, she counselled her children, that which is his and unto God, that which is God's. She never expected to hear her child utter a lie—no less, a lie under oath, an oath to God, in a court of law. To save your mortal skin at the cost of your eternal soul was nothing but a bad Faustian bargain.

That was not how she raised her children. There might be hell to pay, literally and metaphorically, for her oldest son. Even now, Delores has not forgotten Damon's transgression, though she forgives him for doing

something in a moment of fear and weakness
when he thought he had no other option.

Chapter Twenty-Nine

Lies of Omission and Commission

Isaiah Jones visited Damon in jail a third time on Saturday, June 23. He hoped the hiatus gave Damon time to consider that he needed to be honest and give Jones the facts that he required to prepare Damon's defense. Damon sat in jail for almost a month at that point, and the reality of life behind bars started to sink in for him. He did not want to spend the rest of his life there. He knew he had to cooperate with the lawyer his family hired, the best lawyer in town, who just might be able to get him acquitted.

"I have a confession to make," Damon started off the conversation.

"Whoa, son. Hold up right there," Isaiah admonished. "If you are going to tell me you did those terrible things to Leah, then you should consider first what the result of that will be. I would have an ethical obligation to advise you to plead guilty. If you insist on pursuing at trial a story that you are innocent and intend to perjure yourself, I have to advise the court..."

"No, sir. It's nothing like that," Damon countered. "I want to confess to you where I was on the day someone else killed Leah."

Now Jones finally felt like he was making progress; Damon could see it in Isaiah's eyes and his body language, how he leaned forward and tapped his pen to his lips as Damon readied to tell his story. Isaiah thought, "At last. Here comes the alibi!" But the story Damon gave proved both troublesome and difficult to verify.

Damon waffled on telling Jones his alibi due to several reasons. He figured Jones would find it difficult to corroborate. Jones already explained to Damon how alibi defenses work. Damon knew, without a verifiable alibi, he would be made to look the fool on the stand. In the back of his mind, something nagged at his unconscious mind then, but with hindsight twelve years later, he also realized there were reasons his alibi would prove difficult to establish.

Beyond that, his alibi cast Damon in a sordid light, one that would not reflect well on him or his parents, one that would, in fact, mortify them all and subject them to scorn and derision. He was willing to shoulder that scorn; but to thrust it unnecessarily upon his parents was a burden he found hard to bear. Hence, his unwillingness to discuss it before June 23 with Isaiah Jones.

The week Leah died, the riots blew up all across the city. As a young, African American male, Damon watched the events with fascination. He knew so much about racism in his short life, heard it spoken about at home, at church, in the school, on the streets. Daily, he saw the effects. He saw the police pull over black motorists for no reason; he saw or heard the stories of white cops beating black suspects. He had heard the "N" word thrown out casually by whites the way he might shuck off a coat, without caring, without thinking. Those whites either didn't consider the meanness associated with the word or simply didn't care. And his people had to sit back and take it. Like it would never end in his lifetime as it hadn't for four hundred years in this land since the whites first brought slaves over from Africa.

The riots intrigued Damon. He didn't condone the violence; his parents taught him that. But he *understood* the violence, felt the rage his people felt, and silently commiserated them. He wanted to watch it up close and personal. Become an eyewitness to history. Nothing like this had happened in America since the Rodney King riots of '92 (although they would happen again in Ferguson, Flatbush, Oakland, Baltimore, and other cities around the country in the '10s).

Walnut Hills cancelled classes during the riots. Damon did not stay home on the twelfth. He drove over to his school neighborhood and decided to see what the rioters were doing, unfiltered by TV reporters with their carefully edited video and audio. He wanted to see the true riot, in all its ugly glory.

He saw buildings burning, windows broken by the score—no, the hundreds—rocks smashed through them. He saw cars overturned on the street, traces of blood on the roads and sidewalks. He saw people yelling and marching, holding signs, "Honk if you're black!" Which, the black passing motorists did. He saw the police holding a line but not actually engaging the crowd. He heard the yells, the shouts, the chants.

Then he heard someone in the crowd yell, "Get her! She's white!" A woman with blond hair and sunglasses came running out from between an alley chased by several young men. In that moment, Damon faced his first and most important crisis of conscience. A mob was about to assault an innocent person, a woman at that. His parents taught him we must stand up for the poor and the defenseless. He had a choice to make. Allow this poor woman to be beaten by the mob or stand up and defend her, even at, perhaps, a very personal cost of being assaulted himself. Yet, he empathized with the rage the mob felt, which he as a black man could understand, that here was a chance to turn the tables back on the oppressing white people who so long had held the black man down. Why interfere when the tables turned after so many events when whites assaulted or killed blacks and nothing ever happened, no one punished, nothing changed?

At that point in Damon's story, I thought he would tell me he made the right call, that he stood up for this innocent woman. Where is the shame in that? His parents would be proud of his decision.

Damon did stand up for her, called her over to him, shielded her behind his body, picked up an iron bar he found on the street, and brandished it at the oncoming mob. He told them to back off. He made them back off. The woman cowered behind him; he could hear her sniffling, crying, and sobbing. The crowd gave way, called him an Uncle Tom. "You'll get yours someday," one of its members shouted with prescience.

When the small mob turned its attention to another passing (white) motorist in the street, Damon turned his attention to the woman. He pulled her into the alley, out of view of those on the street, and assessed her. He didn't know how old she was, in her thirties, he guessed. She had a knot on her forehead that was starting to bruise with some blood trickling down her face. She said someone hit her in the head with a brick. She had fallen and ripped a hole in her blue jeans, and Damon saw more blood from a scrape on that part of her body. She shook and sobbed. She was scared.

Damon would continue telling Isaiah about Damon's whereabouts on the day Leah died. But he wasn't completely honest, even with his own lawyer. Damon uttered another lie of commission to Isaiah during that meeting. He told him that he had anal sex with Leah. More about that soon.

Chapter Thirty

The Comfort of Strangers

Nine months after 9/11, demographers recorded a curious phenomenon. A spike in birth rates occurred, out of proportion to the usual seasonal odds and variations of live births. On that tragic day, and in the several days after, men and women all over the country huddled together in fear and solace and took what comfort they could, including sexual comfort, from spouses, boyfriends, girlfriends, acquaintances, co-workers, and total strangers.

People seek proximity during times of catastrophe; they seek, sometimes, also to reflect upon their lives. Women who might have decided to put off having a baby, now decide, "This is the time!" The more immediate the danger, the greater the post-disaster effects.

Damon's story of going to watch the riots and then rescuing an innocent is a great story. Left at that, he has nothing to be ashamed of and, indeed, something to be proud of. But it doesn't get him off the hook for those few afternoon hours before Leah died.

Damon walked the woman back to his car; he kept a first aid kit in the trunk. The walk took a couple of minutes, a few blocks, and she walked with a slight limp due to the injured knee, he surmised. He appraised her as they walked. She was in her thirties, he guessed. Pretty good looking, he said, and used the pejorative term 'MILF'[6] when describing her. She was tall, at least five foot eight, nicely built, pretty blue eyes, and she reminded him of this hot math teacher at school, Mrs. Dixon, upon whom all the boys in school had a crush. He visited a white basketball teammate's home once, and all this guy wanted to do was play that old Van Halen song, "Hot for Teacher," and talk about how he'd like to do Mrs. Dixon with his d***, well, you get the idea.

She came from out of town, sent as a special correspondent (read: freelance writer) for *Newsweek*, to write an in-depth article about the riots. She wanted to be on the front lines, to experience its immediacy. She didn't count on becoming a victim of mob violence.

Damon likened her to a war correspondent. He had heard about those wild men and women who ran off to every crazy corner of the world, wherever wars, or conflicts, or genocides, or atrocities took place. Those war correspondents, man, they were crazy. They fucked like bunnies. They'd jump in the sack, or a

---

[6] The term first shows up in general popular culture in the 1990s and now can be found even in the Oxford English Dictionary. It was in common use in 2001 when Damon describes this encounter that took place. For those of you unfamiliar with the term, I suggest you check the OED.

foxhole, at the sound of a mortar shell exploding. It didn't take much to get their hormones raging.

This was, then, he realized in retrospect, what it was like. It was as if he had just been in a war, escaped an ambush, saved the day with his life—his body and his honor—whole and intact. It was a glorious feeling.

And there was this gorgeous woman. She asked him to drive her back to her motel; she didn't think she could drive at all with her injuries. He asked her if he could take her to the hospital, or at least urgent care. She declined. "It's just a scratch," she said.

"That's some scratch; your head is bruised, you got an egg growing upside your skull. It's bleeding, and your knee doesn't look so good, either."

"I've been through worse. I'm a correspondent." (Did he manufacture the word "war" before correspondent when she said it, I wondered almost aloud?)

He pulled the first aid kit out of the trunk, poked around. He put some iodine on her cuts. She winced but didn't cry out. He put some butterfly strips over the cut on her forehead, applied some antibiotic cream, and covered the whole affair with a piece of gauze that he taped to her wound. He had her pull up the leg of her pants, cleaned the scraped knee, and put some iodine on it, as well.

She insisted he just take her back to her motel. Which one, he inquired. The Mallard Motel, she told him. He knew of it. The Mallard sat a few miles up Reading Road from his neighborhood, in the nearby city of Reading. The

Mallard had a proud history dating back to the '40s in the post-WWII era of people travelling by car and staying at motor hotels, while they visited family or friends. Over the years, The Mallard aged like a lot of those old motor courts—not well. By the time I wrote this book, county officials shut The Mallard down; it had become a den of prostitution and drugs, a public nuisance. But in 2001, it flapped along on its last wings, so to speak, unable to take flight away from its deteriorating circumstances.

They arrived back at The Mallard, and she invited him in to her room. She sat on the bed and allowed him to reassess her. He bent down and looked at the knee again. It moved fine, full range of motion, a little tender, but no swelling. He straightened up and cupped her head in his hands, re-examining her head wound. She said it didn't hurt. She put her hand on his forearm and reaching up, with her right arm, put her hand behind his neck and pulled his head down to hers. She kissed him. Gently, on the lips, then with more urgency and need.

Damon didn't respond at first. He was surprised. He was flattered. He was a free man, after all. Leah broke it off with him. He hadn't even seen Leah since Saturday. Um, I mean, he said, since the day before, he corrected himself. In any event, he owed Leah no allegiance; he could be with any woman he wanted, and if this woman wanted him, whether to thank him, or because she was scared, or needy, or found him attractive, it didn't matter. They were two adults, and it felt right.

They made love that afternoon, all afternoon. Past the time when, he didn't even know it then, of course, someone brutally assaulted, raped, and strangled his ex-girlfriend.

When they were through, she told him it was okay; he could just leave. She would get her car later, take a taxi down to get it.

As he left the motel room, the woman, whose name he never asked and which she never gave, snapped off the portable radio that had been playing since the time they entered the room. The last song he heard came from a long-ago dead rocker. Jim Morrison crooned "Love Me Two Times." Except the blonde woman had actually loved Damon three times that afternoon.

Why no one made more of this at Damon's trial astounds me to this very day.

Chapter Thirty-One

Anonymama

"This is," Isaiah told Damon, searching for the right word, "interesting stuff." Jones's usual flair with words escaped him at that moment. "Now all we need to do is verify that you were there all afternoon."

Damon reminded Isaiah that The Mallard wasn't exactly The Omni Netherland Hilton downtown in the Carew Tower. Jones understood Damon's point but told him he would set his investigator onto the matter.

Isaiah Jones would from time to time hire retired police detectives to do investigative work on cases. Most of the time, he engaged Herschel Wingate, one of the CPD's first African Americans to make it to the Homicide bureau. Wingate spent twenty-five years of his life as a beat cop then a detective. During his retirement, he ran a few investigations for Jones and several other attorneys around town, but mostly that was for play money and because, he would admit to me, criminal investigations still intrigued him. He didn't want to completely sever his present persona from that of his past. He saved money on his own, plus pulled a full pension, but the extra income paid for a lot of golf trips all over the USA.

In Cincinnati, Wingate's favorite public course was at a Hamilton County park, Sharon Woods. He liked the difficult course because of all the hills you had to master. The par four #3 was considered the most difficult one in the city. In one of the few happy endings in this story, I can tell you that Wingate died of a massive heart attack on the seventeenth green in 2017 after sinking a fifty-foot putt. Nothing better, I suppose, than to die doing something you love to do. Fortunately for my preparations concerning this book, I had the opportunity to interview Wingate that spring a few months before he died.

Herschel visited Damon in jail on Monday, June 25, to get the backstory for his investigation. Wingate knew The Mallard even though The Mallard nested just outside the northern border of Cincinnati in the city of Reading. He stopped by and, by luck, the clerk that day was the same fellow as the one on duty on April 12. This man worked The Mallard for years. He had seen it all. Drugs. Prostitution. Fights. Murders. Pimps beating up working girls. Johns beating up whores. Black man white woman; white man black woman. Or black on black or white on white. Didn't matter. Some of those events stuck in his mind. But a quiet liaison between a young black man and an older white woman? When the cops weren't even called? Man, he told Wingate, you got to be kidding, right? A white woman renting a unit for a day or a few? To sell sex out of? Happens all the time. They come, and they go. She sells sex for money.

Or for drugs. Shit, if I had a dollar for every time that happened here I'd be a millionaire ten times over.

Herschel asked about surveillance footage. The clerk laughed. The cameras on the property were there for show only. Maybe that'd make some criminal think twice before sticking the clerk up in the office or assaulting somebody in the parking lot. The cameras didn't work and held no film.

What about the register of guests? Remember, this was the time before 9/11. Lodging establishments didn't require boarders to show ID to rent a room. If someone showed ID at The Mallard, you could bet that it was a fake ID. The clerk pulled out the log book from April and found the entry based on the room number Damon gave Herschel. Number 7. According to the log, a woman rented the room the day before Leah's death, April 11, and paid cash for two days. The name, written in a squiggly but legible enough cursive, said "Pat Nixon." Shit, Wingate cursed to himself. Some joker using the name of the dead wife of a dead president. This woman not only wanted to stay anonymous, she wanted to do so with a touch of panache.

Wingate, like most good cops and most good lawyers, has a nose for bullshit. A lot of Damon's story about what this woman told Damon didn't ring true. Why would an out-of-town reporter stay in a dump like The Mallard? Why would she use an alias?

Sometimes, Herschel Wingate's job could be low tech and simple. He next visited a branch of the Hamilton County Public Library a mile up

Reading Road from The Mallard in downtown Reading. He found the magazine section, pulled the *Newsweek* issues from April and flipped through them. He found what he wanted with the Monday, April 23, issue. A reporter filed a two-page article about the riots in Cincinnati. Her name was not Pat Nixon. The reporter was a man, and his name was Christopher Carter.

On Tuesday, June 26, Isaiah returned to the justice center to speak to Damon about what Herschel Wingate found. Bupkus, he told Damon. We got nothing. Your word only. Completely unverifiable. Damon conceded he expected nothing more could be done to establish his whereabouts for the critical few hours when someone killed Leah. "You got yourself one anonymous mama there, Damon," Isaiah told him. "I can think of a lot of reasons she might want to go nameless." (One of those reasons, Isaiah told me but did not share with Damon, was that Damon paid her for sex. Given that Damon was a handsome, personable, affable, and athletic young man at the time, I find it suspect that he would need to pay a woman for sex.) "But, clearly, this lady wants to be an anonymama, and we aren't going to be able to track her down."

Damon told Isaiah that was okay. He didn't want to tell that story on the stand, verifiable or not. He didn't want to look in his mother's eyes across the courtroom and tell in open court, sworn on the Bible, that he had anonymous sex with a woman old enough to be his mother. Delores probably suspected he and Leah had been intimate. They were in a

committed, monogamous relationship. Delores
was a realist. Teenagers were gonna be
teenagers, and sex, well, that was part of life. But
random sex with a woman whose name you
didn't even know or ask? Delores, and Othello,
would surely be disappointed with how they
raised their oldest son.

Chapter Thirty-Two

Release

The Free Damon! campaign worked, and on Friday, June 29, Othello and Delores posted bail of $150 thousand at the clerk's office. The jailers released Damon and gave him back his street clothes. One of them told him in a friendly banter, "I better not see you here again."

The Allbrights headed straight home to North Avondale. They would circle the wagons, Othello thought, using a not so apropos metaphor, in that grand home set on the hill. Damon ate his first home-cooked meal since his arrest on May 25, over a month before. He relished the food. Delores and Othello kicked all the other kids out of the house after dinner, sent them to her sister's house for a sleepover. After the younger children left, the table cleared, and the dishes washed, they moved to the study with the African masks. Damon told me he wanted to wear one. He wanted to transform into something he wasn't and also to shield his parents' gaze from his face. He knew they wanted to discuss the case.

Damon reminded them that Isaiah Jones told him that if he spoke to his parents about the substance of the case, he waived attorney-client privilege. The prosecutor could compel his parents to testify against him at his own trial. He told them that because he wanted to head off any discussion of what he did or didn't do to Leah and where he had been the afternoon of her death. He juggled so many difficult objects at one time, that having to discuss his personal failings with his parents struck him as one too many bowling pins in the air at the same time. He would drop them all.

Othello wasn't buying it. How would they even know that we discussed the case? Maybe Mr. Lehane will ask you on the stand, Damon replied. Then what will you do? Lie to him that we had this discussion tonight? Delores clearly recalls this conversation. She knows teenagers are just learning to become more abstract and less concrete in their thinking. She knows teens love to point out the hypocrisy of their parents. But with the hindsight of years, knowing now that Damon lied to them, when he called them out for the potential lie they might make to a court, when he himself would soon lie to them, the court, and God? The disappointment spread over her face with a visible pall when I interviewed her about this family reunion.

Othello and Delores faced a conundrum. They wanted to help their son. They wanted to know what happened. They thought Damon owed them an explanation. It had nothing to do with the lawyer's fees they paid to Isaiah Jones or the Free Damon! campaign that over a thousand people contributed money to in an effort to get Damon out of jail. Damon was their son, raised by them to be a good citizen and a child of God. They expected him to explain his actions to them, because while he owed a duty as a citizen to the secular world, in the thing that mattered, his life as a human being and a Christian, he should strive to do right and tell the truth.

If, Delores reminded Damon, the prosecutor should call them to the stand and ask them to testify as to what Damon told them, then they would comply. Render unto Caesar. If Damon had nothing to hide, why fear the truth?

What if the truth sheds a bad light upon me, he asked. I mean, I didn't kill Leah. I didn't do any of those things to her. But my explanation will paint me as an unworthy person, in your eyes and in God's eyes. How will you ever look at me again and not think the worst of me?

Othello assured his son that Damon need not worry about his parents' opinion. They loved him, knew what a fine young man he was, just as they had raised them. If he made mistakes, well, Damon, you are a human being. We all make mistakes. I have, your mother has. If you seek God's forgiveness, he will forgive you. Certainly, as your parents, we will.

Damon told his parents that night the story of how he went to watch the riots. How he saved the blonde woman from the crowd. Before his parents could even interject what a fine thing he had done, he let them know there were worse things to tell them. He told them how he drove the reporter back to her motel. How she invited him in. How she initiated the sex, but how he made no effort to reject the offer—how, yes, he did accept her advances. (He spared his parents the details of the once, twice, three encounters they had during the course of that afternoon. The general idea was, he told me, more than sufficient to make his point.)

He watched his mother's face, the pride he saw when he described saving the woman. Then the shock that fell over her face like a veil when he told them of his anonymous tryst. She surprised him again when her face drew more steady, proud even, that her son had told the truth even when he faced reprobation.

One more matter to discuss, Othello said. Damon knew what was coming. Othello and Delores knew enough about the case as reported by the media to know that a DNA match linked Damon's semen to Leah's body. They didn't know much about DNA, but just as intelligent people, wondered how, assuming the two kids actually had sex on Saturday before Leah's murder, his DNA still resided in her body five days later. Did they have sex again, asked Othello. Yes, Damon admitted, wiggling the truth like a worm stuck on a fish hook, we did. The day *before* somebody else killed her.

Chapter Thirty-Three

Pretrial Maneuvers

Matt Lehane, unlike Isaiah Jones, is an actual chess player. He enjoys the metaphor of trial strategy as a chess game. Lehane liked playing "chess" with Jones and knew he would have his hands full with this particular opponent. The first salvo fired was Isaiah's request for discovery pursuant to the Rules of Criminal Procedure. Discovery was had. Lehane waited for Jones's next move, which, as expected, was a motion to suppress Damon's statement to Bergdorf that the last time Damon had seen Leah was Saturday, April 7.

Jones filed that motion on Monday, July 23, one week before the pretrial hearing. Lehane smiled when he reviewed the motion. This little motion told Lehane so much about Damon's trial strategy. Matt Lehane knew the strengths and limitations of his case, just as Isaiah Jones did. Damon could defeat the DNA evidence in one of two ways. The DNA evidence was incorrect—it was planted by the police, or the lab committed an error. That dog don't hunt, Lehane mused, using a saying his dad, who grew up in the South, often verbalized. Or Damon could get on the stand and testify that he and Leah had sex again

215

on the day before her death, hence his DNA still resided in her body when the coroner did the autopsy. And when Damon took the stand to testify, Lehane would impeach him with his prior statement to Bergdorf. Either Damon Allbright had sex with Leah twenty-four hours before her death or not. In a way, it didn't matter. If he said he did, and even if he actually did, then he lied to Bergdorf. Now Lehane will tell the jury that Damon lied, either to the police, or to you today on the stand. In either case, you can't believe his testimony. He is a liar. Now that you know he is a liar, you can't believe his story, whatever his story is. Maybe he had sex with Leah the day before, consensual as he claims. And maybe he raped her, beat her, and strangled her to death, while she was bound in trusses. How can you take his word when he lies to you?

Lehane smiled with grim satisfaction. He had Damon. Lehane also knew that Fred "the Hammer" Burger would overrule Jones's motion to suppress. Guaranteed.

Matt did wonder why Isaiah filed the motion to suppress. Isaiah knew that Burger would most likely overrule the motion. Certainly, that set something up for appeal, that the judge allowed Damon's impeaching statement when the police obtained it in violation of Damon's right against self-incrimination. But even a court of appeals would likely find that a reasonable decision by the trial judge. Why was Jones telegraphing his defense without any real hope of a favorable outcome at trial on appeal? This question vexed Matt Lehane.

Jones also filed a motion *in limine*, which requests the court to block the opposing party from using evidence that is so inflaming of jurors' sensibilities that the prejudice against the aggrieved party outweighs the probative value of the evidence. Jones filed to exclude certain photographs of Leah's body, such as crime scene photos and autopsy phots. He didn't expect Burger to grant the motion. Indeed, in his experience, those photos paled in comparison with some of the more horrific ones he had to contend with on other cases. But, he had to make an effort and protect the record for Damon's appeal.

On July 30, Judge Burger brought the lawyers before the bench to discuss pretrial matters on the record. Often, he would hold these conferences in his chambers, but for this trial, with these stakes, he wanted it held in open court with a court reporter making a transcript. Nothing he did pretrial would be grounds for an appeal by either side.

Ben and Sarah Marcus attended the pretrial. So did I and my counterpart from the *Enquirer*. Local TV reporters came, also. I tried to ask the Marcuses after the hearing their impressions, but they declined to talk to me, as they had on every occasion up to that point that I attempted to interview them.

Isaiah's first motion asked the court to suppress Damon's statement to Bergdorf on the grounds that it violated his Fifth and Fourteenth Amendment rights under the Constitution as interpreted by the landmark case, *Miranda v. Arizona* (1966). That case established the

Miranda rights that have become part and parcel of so many television shows and movies about the police, not to mention actual police procedure. In a nutshell, suspects have to be advised of their right to remain silent and their right to counsel. Burger overruled Damon's motion because there was no indication that he was either in police custody at the time of his statement or even a suspect. That interview occurred so early on in the investigation that the police only searched for information as to what happened to Leah, and they had no reason to suspect at the time that Damon was involved.

Burger then overruled the motion *in limine*, noting that the photographs did not rise to the level of prejudicial inflammation of a jury's mind-set. So far, Lehane threw two strikes against Jones.

Burger moved on to the next pretrial issue, setting a trial date. Damon had speedy trial rights that the judge had to honor unless waived. Jones told me that at that point, the strategy was to "Bring it on!" He saw no point in delay. Lehane knew, Isaiah surmised, that Damon would take the stand and say he had sex with Leah the day before her death. Isaiah didn't want to give Lehane any time to go out and find a witness, say an ex-girlfriend, who would testify that Damon liked rough sex, or tied her up, or, God forbid, even raped her. The sooner this thing went to trial, the better. Plus, if Damon won an acquittal, the trial would be over soon enough that Damon wouldn't even miss a day of class at the University of Cincinnati when classes resumed in the fall. Burger kept the originally blocked off week of August 20 for the trial.

In the weeks between Damon's release on bail and the trial, Isaiah never stopped looking for the mystery woman at The Mallard. Nor did he give up on trying to find that other woman in the car, with perhaps her male friend in it, that Alice Bowman told the detectives about. Herschel Wingate went through the State's discovery package, tracked down all the surveillance cameras within a one-mile radius of the Marcus house, and went door-to-door in the neighborhood looking for private security cameras that homeowners in the neighborhood might have employed. He found grainy images of the woman and the car, but he could neither identify the make and model and certainly not a license plate number. He did see a shadow on the passenger side of the vehicle, but whether it was a human, or male, or the person who assaulted Leah, he had no idea.

Isaiah Jones told Wingate that he wasn't terribly disappointed. Sometimes, it's better to point out the existence of a phantom at a criminal trial then to actually bring the phantom into court.

Chapter Thirty-Four

Summer in the City

The trial started three weeks after Burger conducted the pretrial. In between those dates, Cincinnatians dealt with the aftermath of the riots. The sun beat down on the city in July and August in that year. Multiple days recorded highs in the mid-nineties.

Black leaders called for a boycott of downtown businesses. Within a year, that boycott yielded an estimated economic impact in excess of $10 million. As mentioned above, numerous African American entertainers cancelled engagements to perform in Cincinnati.

Gentrification of Over-the-Rhine, which began before Stephen Roach shot Tim Thomas, continued. That gentrification process goes on to this day. Now you can find condominiums that cost over a million dollars on blocks just north of Central Parkway that, before the old buildings were torn down, lower income residents could rent for $300 per month. Restaurants, micro-breweries, and upscale shops opened.

Not all civic leaders opposed changes. City council took a long look at police procedures. Local Fortune 500 companies such as Proctor & Gamble, Fifth Third Bank, and Kroger supported changes such as investment in local schools and minority hiring.

The lawsuit that Al Gerhardstein filed on behalf of the ACLU and the Cincinnati Black United Front went to mediation in June 2001. It resulted in a groundbreaking collaborative agreement between the plaintiffs, the city, and the police union. The agreement revamped how the city would recruit and train police. It also created a process to investigate and track police use of force. A federal monitor would follow the police department to ensure compliance with the agreement. The CPD would go on to have officers wear bodycams, a process nowadays implemented on an almost national basis. Some years later, in 2015, a University of Cincinnati police officer shot and killed an unarmed black driver, Samuel Dubose, during a routine traffic stop. The UC officer wore a bodycam (as UC officers had since 2004), and the case resulted in charges filed against the officer within ten days.

By 2010, the Rand Corporation conducted a study of how the Collaborative Agreement was working. The report found no difference between CPD stops of black drivers from similarly situated non-black drivers. Some individual officers continued to stop more black than non-black drivers; but this constituted a remarkable change from 2001 when police pulled over twice as many black drivers as whites.

Over the summer, the two largest media events concerned the riots and the Allbright trial. They consumed the print, digital, and on-air media. Damon's trial coverage created a duel

221

between the *Tribune* and the *Enquirer*, each paper trying to scoop the other with in-depth coverage. The sort of coverage that the local TV stations could not compete with, with their limited two- or, perhaps, three-minute air articles. Local radio stations, though, competed heavily with the newspapers. There, radio talk show personalities spent hours venting about the riots and the Allbright trial. They brought on-air guests and callers by the droves who further fanned the flames of racial tensions that summer.

In the USA and the world at large, events continued to unfold during the summer of 2001. In his first event at Daytona since his father died at the Daytona 500, Dale Earnhardt Jr. won his first race, the Pepsi 400, on July 7. The American League won the All-Star game 4-1 on July 10.

On August 1, Alabama Supreme Court Chief Justice Roy Moore installed a monument of the Ten Commandments in the judiciary building. That led to a lawsuit that resulted in the removal of the monument and Moore from his office.

On August 9, President George W. Bush announced his support for limited testing of embryonic stem cells.

The band Nickelback released the song "How You Remind Me" on August 21. *Billboard* named it song of the year for 2002. (That song holds a cherished spot on my favorites list on my iPhone.) A plane crashed in the Bahamas on August 25, killing the singer Aaliyah and eight others.

On August 23, the third day of Damon's trial, an Egyptian by the name of Mohammad

Atta flew from Florida to purchase the plane tickets for September 11. He would fly American Airlines Flight 11 into the North Tower of the World Trade Center at 8:46 a.m. nineteen days later. Among the casualties from that day were four people who called Cincinnati home.

While life went on for Americans and Cincinnatians in general, for Matt Lehane and Isaiah Jones, the last few weeks before trial brought a stupendous uptick in work for prepping the most significant murder trial to hit a Hamilton County courtroom in decades.

Chapter Thirty-Five

Final Trial Preparations and the Trial

Begins

During the rest of the time between trial and pretrial, Isaiah Jones hunkered down with Damon Allbright and others discussing final trial strategies, conducting witness interviews and testimony preparation for witnesses, including Damon's. Isaiah also started preparing for *voir dire*,[7]—the process of picking a jury, his opening statement, his cross-examinations of prosecution witnesses, and his closing argument. All of this work consumed so much of Isaiah's time that he turned over his other cases to an associate attorney in his office. Isaiah reviewed the prosecution's witness list with Damon and explained what he, Isaiah, expected each of these witnesses would testify about. The only name on the list for which he had no clue was that of Damon's friend, Dante Braxton. What would Dante possibly testify about? Damon said he had

[7] From the French, "to see, to speak," an opportunity for the lawyers to talk directly to the jury pool in order to pick a jury as beneficial to their side as possible.

no idea. Isaiah told Damon to get right over to Dante and find out; he is your friend, right?

Isaiah spent hours working with Damon on his trial testimony. The easy part would be the questions soft-lobbed to Damon. Damon felt beat up when Isaiah played the role of Matt Lehane, who would get his licks in on cross-examination. Damon told me that Isaiah's role-playing brutalized him. But, he conceded, having been through it once before Lehane got to him, he felt prepared and did as well as he hoped he would on the stand. He also told me that Isaiah pushed him harder than Lehane did.

One last pretrial maneuver Isaiah punted on. He talked with Damon about Damon's alibi for his whereabouts April 12, the day someone murdered Leah. Jones had no fact witnesses who could establish alibi. His investigator, Herschel Wingate, found no one from The Mallard who could testify that he or she saw Damon on that date at the relevant times. The mystery woman, who certainly did not work for *Newsweek*, either didn't exist (possible, Jones admitted to me, doubting Damon's credibility here) or couldn't be found. Without a fact witness, there was no point in presenting an alibi. Who would testify? Damon? Ridiculous. Besides, Isaiah pointed out to Damon, as sordid as the case sounded, Damon's story that he and Leah "hooked up one last time" by itself sounded so much better than Damon's proffered truth. If Damon had anonymous sex with a woman he didn't even know the very next day, the somewhat "Boy Scout" like image of Damon takes a hit, something that would probably trouble the jury.

They agreed not to file a motion for alibi. Worst case scenario, Jones told me later, it would be another ground for appeal based on ineffective assistance of counsel.

Monday, August 20, dawned hot and steamy. Fred Burger's courtroom on the fifth floor of the Hamilton County Courthouse burst to the seams with all the participants to the trial, the jury pool, the Marcus and Allbright families, and, of course, the press, myself included.

Common pleas judges might not like murder trials, but they like the publicity the trials bring. Publicity helps with name recognition and getting re-elected for another six years on the bench. Burger warmly welcomed the jury[8] pool, and thanked them all for participating in this amazing civic duty and protection for criminal defendants that dated back to England, all the way to 1219 or 1670, depending upon what history book you wanted to rely on. That generated a few muted laughs from the jury pool. Back in 2001, the clerk of court picked a jury pool from the list of registered voters in Hamilton County. Since many African Americans did not register to vote, despite the large number of them residing in the county, particularly the city of Cincinnati, many blacks were never called to serve on juries. Typical petit juries back then consisted of ten or eleven whites and one or two blacks. The parties would also pick two alternate jurors in case one

---

[8] The word "jury" derives from the Latin term "jurati" meaning "to be sworn."

or two of the seated members got sick, died, or disqualified.

Voir dire progressed, and the parties agreed to a jury all within the first day of trial. The jury consisted of ten whites and two African Americans, six men and six women. The alternates were a white man and an African American woman. Unlike rich defendants, say O. J. Simpson, Jones could not afford to hire a jury consultant to help him pick the jury. The fee for one of those experts would equal almost as much as Damon's family paid Jones to handle the entire case. Isaiah had to rely on his experience as a litigator. He wanted more blacks on the jury, but that was a systemic issue that he could not argue at the trial court level. He noted that Lehane never challenged a black juror peremptorily,[9] which might have led to a Batson[10] challenge.

---

[9] Lawyers can make two kinds of challenges to prospective jurors. A challenge "for cause" entails a scenario where a juror holds a preconceived notion, such as the defendant is guilty, or would refuse to consider a death penalty, or is related to a party or one of the witnesses. A "peremptory" challenge allows the lawyers to summarily dismiss a juror for no given reason at all, other than the lawyer suspects the juror wouldn't vote in the client's favor.

[10] Because lawyers, in the past, often peremptorily dismissed African American jurors, the Supreme Court held that the challenging side must show that the challenge was not a race-based cause for the challenge, such as the juror

Isaiah wanted a mix of people on the jury; all he needed was one strong holdout to vote for an acquittal, and he would end up with a hung jury. That would avoid a conviction for Damon, but might lead to a re-trial at the prosecutor's discretion. Isaiah knew that prosecutors typically retry cases where the jury voted strongly, but not unanimously, in favor of guilt. Anything nine to three or better in favor of conviction, the prosecutor would retry the case. At a minimum, then, he needed at least four jurors to vote for acquittal. Given the racial politics of the case, Isaiah didn't want a retrial. He wanted an acquittal. To garner an acquittal, Isaiah needed a unanimous verdict, just as the prosecutor would need to gain a conviction. He wanted religious people, but not too religious. Religious but not one willing to commit a young man to damnation because he had premarital sex with his girlfriend. He wanted people suspicious of the cops and the "system," who perceived and acknowledged the little injustices that those in power perpetrated on those in society without power.

The parties agreed to a jury by 4:30 that afternoon. They were duly sworn in. Given the politics of the case, the judge sequestered the jury in a local hotel downtown, and the bailiff made the jurors surrender their cell phones to him. They would not have telephone access or access to the media, whether print or electronic,

---

had spent time in jail before. <u>Batson v. Kentucky</u>, 476 U.S. 79 (1986).

during the remainder of the trial. Trial would commence on Tuesday, at 9:00 a.m.

Judge Burger's courtroom burst to the seams again on August 21. Although all those prospective jurors disappeared, other people took their seats. Courthouse watchers, lawyers who had nothing better to do but learn from two master litigators, friends of the Marcus and Allbright families, all these people filled the seats.

Matt Lehane led off with his opening statement. Opening statement is the lawyer's opportunity to tell the jury what the facts of the case will demonstrate. This is not a time to make arguments or be impassioned. "Just the facts, ma'am," applies to opening statements. Isaiah Jones followed. An hour elapsed from the time that Lehane stood up and Jones sat down. Lehane called his first witness at 10:30 a.m. after a short recess.

Chapter Thirty-Six

The Prosecutor's Case: Motive

Matt Lehane called Sarah Marcus as his first witness. The purpose was twofold. First, Sarah would testify as to what a wonderful daughter Leah was. Second, she was a fact witness useful to establish the prosecution's timeline of the case.

I watched Sarah's stoic demeanor as she walked to the witness box. She dressed in a navy business suit, low heels, subtle makeup, and the only jewelry she wore other than her wedding band was a pair of small earrings. Lehane walked her and the jury through the testimony. The jury learned that the Marcus parents were part of an exclusive club of Cincinnatians, a true power couple. But while they were moneyed, they fought for the common person, Ben in his law practice and Sarah in her non-profit assisting the mentally ill. She described her two children, mostly talking about Leah. She painted a verbal picture of a smart, talented, affable, caring young woman who would have made a lasting mark in the world—had she only lived. She was going to go to Harvard and then medical school to become a pediatric neurosurgeon and still would have found time to serenade people with her extraordinary ability to play the piano. She asked to play two of the many video recordings of Leah's piano music that she had compiled over the years. Jones thought of objecting but realized that would only alienate the jury. Instead, he would use it to his advantage and find a video of Damon singing, which he would present during the defense case. Judge Burger allowed the videos in the absence of an objection. The first was from the Walnut Hills holiday production the previous winter, where Leah played "Carol of the Bells," a standard Christmas piece written in 1914 by the Ukrainian composer, Mykola Leontovych. The video lasted three and a half minutes. The second video Sarah showed Leah's appearance at Corbett Auditorium at the University of Cincinnati's world-famous College Conservatory of Music, where Leah competed in a juniors piano performance. At that event, she played her signature piece, the Franz Liszt "Hungarian Rhapsody #2," which ran for almost ten minutes. The videos astonished not only the jurors but the spectators and courtroom personnel. As I watched the jury and the courtroom as a whole, I saw tears well up in many eyes.

When I spoke with Sarah Marcus in 2016 about the trial, she told me the ache in her heart never went away, even fifteen years later. But back then, in August, a mere four months after Leah's murder, the pain was so raw and palpable, like nerves fired by a Taser, that she had a difficult time keeping herself composed on the stand while she testified. In those days, she relived the nightmare both in her waking life and her dreams. To then have to speak about it out loud, in front of a panel of strangers, describing finding your daughter naked, bound, bludgeoned, and strangled to death was almost more than she could bear to do. But she had to do it. She had to tell the story.

Sarah testified about the state of alert that many Cincinnatians felt during the week of the riots. With two working parents and school cancelled, Sarah made Leah promise that she would stay in the locked house all day until Sarah got home from work. She told the jury she left early on Thursday, April 12, to check on her daughter. She described the scene she found in the front hall, the blood-drenched carpet, the trail of blood leading up the stairs to Leah's bedroom, bursting into the room and finding her daughter on the rug, naked, hands bound behind her back, blood pooling from a head wound, and a cord wrapped tightly around her neck. She told the jury how she checked for signs of life and finding none, sobbing. That was when Sarah's stoicism failed her, and she had to take a moment to compose herself as she started to cry. She described how she didn't want the first responders staring at her daughter's naked body so she covered Leah with the comforter from the bed, how she called 9-1-1 and waited in her daughter's room until Officer Noble rang the doorbell a few minutes later. She let the jury know the timing of all these events, as Sarah commanded an unusual ability to keep track of her time given the busy nature of her work. Lehane asked Sarah if she had any idea who might have wanted to harm her daughter. Isaiah objected. Overruled. She started to describe the conversation she had with Leah on the Saturday before her death after she returned from her date with Damon. Isaiah again objected on the basis of hearsay and asked for a sidebar. The judge quickly overruled the objection out of the jury's hearing and allowed Sarah to testify that Leah told her that she broke up with Damon because they both would graduate in June and head off to different universities in the fall. There. Lehane, with his first witness, established a motive. Leah identified the man sitting at the defense table as Damon Allbright, Leah's ex-boyfriend.

Isaiah Jones kept his eye on the jurors as Sarah testified. He knew Lehane led with a powerful and poignant witness, whose testimony would set the tone for the trial. He could already see jurors looking over at Damon, trying to reconcile the mild-mannered, handsome young man in his own navy suit with someone who could possibly do the things the State accused him of. When it was his turn to cross-examine Sarah, he told the court he had no questions. No point in badgering the bereaved mother. He would only earn the scorn of the jury. Sarah left the witness box, her testimony complete, and no one expecting to call her again as a witness, she stayed in the courtroom for the remainder of the trial as a spectator, sitting next to Ben in the first row of seats behind the prosecutor's table.

Matt Lehane next called Damon's friend and teammate, Dante Braxton, to the stand. The sheer size of Dante's frame suggested something big was to come for the jury, and Lehane did not disappoint. Lehane did not expect Braxton to assist in testifying against Damon; he knew he might have to ask the court to allow him to treat Dante as a hostile witness, which would allow him to use leading questions rather than open-ended questions. Lehane did not know that Jones had already prepared Dante for this part and that Jones would clean up the testimony on his cross-examination.

Lehane asked him about the incident at the school cafeteria on Monday, April 9. Dante admitted he walked over to the table where Leah sat with her friend Tory Maxwell and several other girls. He started to testify that he told Leah that, "Damon told me you broke it off with him. He's upset. Very upset. I think you should go over to him and tell him you've changed your mind. You'll take him back. Otherwise, he says, you'll be sorry." Again, Jones leapt to his feet objecting that what Damon told Dante constituted hearsay and should not be admitted. As expected, Judge Burger allowed the testimony because the Rules of Evidence allow for such statements made by a party opponent. Lehane thought he scored more points with the jury by having Damon's good friend testify against him as to the nature of a threat made by a towering man to a petite woman.

But on cross, Jones rehabilitated Dante's testimony. Dante said Damon never actually told Dante that Leah would be sorry. Dante made that up. He only tried to help Damon get back together with Leah and wanted to impress upon her the seriousness of her mistake. Damon never said that, "You'll be sorry." Dante himself was now sorry in retrospect that he tried to help Damon, because his statement was now being used to hurt his friend.

On redirect, Lehane made it clear to the jurors that Dante and Damon were best friends since elementary school, the implication being that Dante would help Damon out with his trial testimony. Still, Jones's cross-examination undercut Lehane's theory of motive a bit.

Matt Lehane loves to try cases. He is the kind of lawyer who could have gone into private practice years ago and made a fortune in civil litigation. But Matt's passion and upbringing dedicated him to a life of service to his community. He figured it was better to keep the bad guys off the streets of Hamilton County (and elsewhere, as he was often called in as a special prosecutor in surrounding county cases) than to make lots of money. He anticipated that Jones would posit some more benign explanation for Dante's statement.

Lehane called Tory Maxwell as his next witness. She testified about the lunchroom conversation. While Tory is a little taller than Leah was, at five foot six, Dante still towers over Tory by thirteen inches. Not to mention 125 pounds of pure muscle. She testified that no one at the lunch table, most importantly herself, took Dante's statement as anything but a threat. She knew Dante from around school. He was a fun guy, a jokester, a backslapper, a loudmouth. "But that day," she said, "he wore his game face, the one when he'd pile drive an opposing lineman into the ground on a running play or when he'd take a charge on the basketball court. He wasn't fooling around that day."

On cross, Isaiah elicited that Tory didn't know Dante all that well. Not well enough to be able to tell if he was serious, just joking around, or even telling a little white lie about what Damon did or actually didn't say. She had to admit she didn't know if Damon made the statement to Dante or not.

All in all, though, Lehane performed credibly in establishing that most important non-element of a case that jurors want to hear about—motive.

Chapter Thirty-Seven

The Prosecutor's Case: First Response

and Investigation

The court adjourned at noon for a lunch recess, and Lehane started up the afternoon testimony with Miranda Noble, the police officer first on the scene following Sarah Marcus's 9-1-1 call. She testified that she heard the dispatch call and so became the first officer to respond to the scene. She described the house and finding Leah's body, moving the comforter off the body, checking for signs of life and finding none, calling in for detectives and criminalists, as well as the coroner. She shepherded Sarah Marcus to a safe room in the house and checked the house for the presence of a perpetrator. Finding none, she secured the crime scene pending arrival of other personnel.

Simon Bergdorf testified next. He described what he found in the front hall, such as the blood-soaked rug and the bronze statue. He told of the trail of blood leading up the stairs and down the second-floor hallway to Leah's room. He described the body, the warmth of the skin, the lividity, the burst petechiae in the eyes, the cord around the neck, and the bleeding head wound. He described the belts that bound Leah's hands and those still tied to the bedposts, along with the blood-stained sheets. He described interviewing Damon the day after the murder when Damon told Simon that Damon had not seen Leah since the Saturday before the murder.

Isaiah Jones kept Bergdorf on the stand quite a while during cross. The police found fingerprints on the bronze statue, correct? Yes. But they didn't match Leah's, Ben's, Sarah's, Tory's, the maid's, or any other regular family or friends who visited the Marcus home.

Oh, by the way, you found the fingerprints of Leah's neighbor, Vernon Banks, on the outside window sill of Leah's piano room, right? Yes. Jones had Bergdorf testify about the creepy neighbor, his four convictions for child sex abuse and the time he spent in state prison, the porn they found on his computer, including child pornography and torture porn. And last, you did not find Damon's prints on the bronze statue, correct? Yes, Bergdorf admitted.

Jones had Bergdorf testify about interviewing the Marcuses' neighbor, Alice Bowman, how, based on her statements, they looked for the mystery blonde woman with the car. Jones set up a video monitor in the courtroom to show the jury some of the grainy surveillance footage that Bergdorf and Nowakowski reviewed trying to identify the car and its driver. Wasn't that shape in the passenger seat another person? Bergdorf would not commit to that.

Lehane called as his next witness the CPD criminalist, Jim Fallwell, a ten-year veteran of the department. He told the jury about the crime scene photos that he took. When Lehane offered some as evidence, Jones objected, but Burger overruled him on the basis that the probative nature of the pictures outweighed any prejudicial effect to Damon. Fallwell told about collecting evidence at the scene of the crime, such as the belts, the bedclothes, vacuuming for trace evidence such as hairs, and all the fingerprints he collected. He also told about meeting Damon later at the police station and collecting a buccal swab for a DNA sample to match against the DNA taken from the victim's body and the crime scene. He testified about the head and pubic hairs he collected, both from Damon and from the comforter and the bedsheets.

Lehane's next witness scored significant points with the jury. This was Ajay Patel, the serologist with a PhD from the crime lab, who did the DNA analysis at the crime laboratory. He walked the jury through DNA sequencing and testing, how he compared Damon's buccal swab samples to the samples collected from Leah's mouth, vagina, and rectum. He told the jury Damon's DNA matched that collected from Leah's body, and that the odds of a such a match being someone other than Damon amounted to one in a quadrillion. That astronomical sounding number startled the jury. You could see eyes getting large inside heads and then swift looks over to Damon.[11]

---

[11] Patel also testified about the hair analysis he made regarding the pubic hairs and head hairs

On cross, Isaiah Jones also scored some notable points. Jones asked Patel if he could tell when the semen was deposited in Leah's body. That afternoon? That morning? The day before? In each case, Patel had to answer, "I don't know." (This set up Damon's subsequent testimony that he had voluntary sex with Leah the day prior to her death.) Jones got the witness to admit that if Damon had sex with Leah up to twenty-four hours prior to her death, his semen would be still inside Leah's body and thus it was possible that the DNA match came from a prior sexual encounter, not necessarily from the day Leah died. Patel testified that the DNA lifted from the scrapings under Leah's fingernails did not match Damon's. Jones would later put that testimony to good use at closing arguments.

By this time in the day, the whole afternoon spent, the judge called a recess in the trial. The jury went into sequestration. The case continued on Wednesday, August 22, with Lehane's final witness, Allison Pollard, the deputy coroner.

Pollard testified in dozens of homicide trials over the years, most with Lehane as the lead prosecutor. The two professionals have a well-synched choreography that impresses jurors. Pollard herself makes a striking witness, tall, authoritative, expert. She testified that not only did she perform the autopsy, but that she

---

found on the bed, comforter, and Leah's body. The weak evidence there showed these hairs came from an African American male, but no one could conclude that these were Damon's hairs.

responded to the crime scene and examined the body *in situ* as well as relevant rooms in the house. She testified about the condition of the body, the lividity, the body temperature of 95 degrees, and how body temperature cools off from the moment of death at one to two degrees per hour. She described the ligature marks and how the belts matched the marks on Leah's body. She told the jury of her suspicion of sexual assault based upon bruising around the labia and anus. Pollard noted the debris underneath Leah's nails and how she would later scrape them at the autopsy looking for DNA of a suspect that Leah might have fought with. She matched the bronze statute to the wound on Leah's skull. Next, she testified about the autopsy and the results. The blow to the head caused a lot of bleeding by way of a deep laceration, but did not cause a skull fracture nor Leah's death. Noting the sexual assault, she took DNA swabs from Leah's body and scraped the undersides of Leah's nails and then sent the samples to the crime lab. She told the jury that Leah died from strangulation, thereby, causing asphyxia. In the absence of a witness to the death, she could not give an exact time of death. But based on the lividity, body temperature, and lack of rigor mortis, she opined that death occurred on the afternoon of April 12. Couching her language in the standard opinion language used by coroners, she posited within a reasonable degree of medical certainty that "Leah Marcus died on Thursday, April 12, 2001, and that the manner of death was homicide, by party or parties unknown."

On cross, Jones elicited from Pollard that someone struck Leah on the head with something heavy like the bronze statue and that blow rendered her unconscious. Pollard snuck in her response that the assailant was right handed given the blow to the left temple of Leah's head. Jones got Pollard to concede that no one could tell for sure whether the semen ended up in Leah's body before or after her death. Jones would later argue that the jury can't convict Damon of rape if Leah was already dead when the semen was deposited. At best, the jury could find Damon committed gross abuse of a corpse. The best Pollard could indicate was that given the bruising, someone had either sexually assaulted Leah or Leah had engaged in rough sex.

With Pollard's testimony concluded, Lehane rested the State's case. Jones made a motion for a Rule 29 dismissal of the case. Burger overruled it outside of the jury's hearing. Burger adjourned court at 3:30 rather than make Jones start his defense late in the day. The trial resumed on Thursday morning, August 23.

Chapter Thirty-Eight

The Defense Case

While the case proceeded at the courthouse, the media coverage continued unabated. The papers, the TV, and radio stations saturated the public with stories, editorials, programs, and trash-talking about the Allbright murder trial. Print and television journalism proved objective, but talk radio hosts brought up the race card *ad nauseum*. Callers railed for or against Damon, the undertone being that if you were black, you thought Damon just another victim of racism and the riots, and if you were white, you thought a black man was about to get away with murder again, à la O. J. Simpson. Polls showed that eighty percent of blacks thought Damon innocent and seventy-eight percent of whites thought him guilty.

Isaiah Jones began Damon's defense with a classic defense strategy, demonstrating the good character of his client. He called several character witnesses, starting with Scott Mansard, the Walnut Hills High School boys basketball coach, who testified about Damon's skill, leadership, and work ethic. Next, Jones brought in Stella Sanderson, one of Damon's teachers at school, who shepherded him through history and civics classes over three years. She testified about his almost straight "A" grade point average, how Damon was planning to go to the University of Cincinnati in the fall, how he was polite in class, engaged, and tutored elementary school students from a disadvantaged school on the weekends. Carl Lamott, an associate pastor at Mt. Carmel Baptist Church, testified about Damon's work with the youth ministry, how he went to Africa, twice, over the summers of his sophomore and junior years to do missions, and how he attended church every Sunday.

Next, Isaiah called Alice Bowman, the eighty-year-old neighbor of the Marcuses who saw the "mystery woman" drive into the neighborhood, park her car, and walk back to Leah's house on the day Leah died. She explained how the driver drove in fast, parked, got out of her car, yet walked back down the street the way she came in to approach Leah's house. The driver was a blonde woman, somewhere between twenty and forty years old, wearing a baseball cap with her ponytail sticking out the back of the cap. This was at 1:48, she testified, because she recalled checking her watch.

On cross, Lehane had to take it easy so as not appear to be beating up on someone's cute old grandmother. Alice had, in fact, not been wearing her distance glances when she saw this woman. No one else was with the woman. Alice didn't actually see this woman go up or into the Marcus home.

After a break for lunch, the trial resumed. The part everyone—even the jury sensed it— was waiting for was at hand. Damon took the stand to testify in his own defense. Many criminal defendants choose to exercise their right to remain silent. Taking the stand sets a defendant up for a great risk. Prosecutors are trial lawyers who specialize in cross-examining witnesses. Most prosecutors can get a defendant wrapped up in a lie so fast the defendant either doesn't see it coming or the prosecutor already had him boxed in based, usually, on a taped confession the defendant already had given to the police. Defendants who testify get filleted, grilled, and eaten by prosecutors when they choose to take the stand. But Damon's defense required that he testify. Without his testimony that he had consensual sex with Leah, he left the jury to the obvious conclusion that he did, in fact, rape and kill Leah.

Damon took the stand and started his testimony. He told of his upbringing in his family, his strong family; his father, the minister; his mother, the caregiver and volunteer to the community and church. He told about his school work, his missions, his work with the youth ministry, and his singing. Jones presented a video showcasing Damon's singing talent, a video from church where Damon sang "Amazing Grace." As with Leah's performance, the jury watched with awe at the magical voice of the young man.

Damon explained how he met Leah in seventh grade at Walnut Hills and ignored her. Until the eighth-grade music class, when he saw her perform on the piano. He told the jury how he approached Leah and suggested they perform together and how she agreed and thus began a

245

five-year collaboration. He described how, over time, he became attracted to her as a potential girlfriend and how he finally found the wherewithal to invite her out on a date in sophomore year.

He described their gentle, loving relationship. She told him she was a virgin and wouldn't agree to have sex with him until well into their junior year. No, she wasn't into rough sex and nor was he. He thought of sex in almost religious tones, that it was soul-freeing, a way of finding God in another person, and bringing both of you closer together as well as closer to God. (Lehane would point out on cross that the whole sexual/spiritual connection was intended for married couples according to church doctrine.)

Damon told the jury about his last date with Leah on Saturday, April 7, when Leah told him she wanted to break up. No, he wasn't upset. Sad. But he expected it. They were both going off to different universities, hundreds of miles apart from each other. He loved Leah but didn't consider her the love of his life. He was her first love, but she did not consider him the love of her life. She had so much to offer the world, to see and to do, that he knew she would have other lovers and maybe, someday, find a man she would choose to be her husband. She was going places; she had a career to start, music to pursue. She was one of those one in a million people with that "it" factor that never would be happy tied down in Cincinnati with a routine and mundane life that most of us accept as not only our due in life but as welcome. She would be the first neurosurgeon ever to perform at Carnegie Hall.

She was special. And he loved her and never would hurt her or do those things the State accused him of.

Damon did tell Dante Braxton about the breakup, but he never told him that "Leah would be sorry." Nor did Damon tell him to say anything at all to Leah during lunch that day, least of all to make any threats to her. That was a frolic and detour that Dante engaged on his own without Damon's knowledge or blessing.

Jones asked Damon when was the last time he saw Leah. Damon told the jury that was Wednesday, April 11. The administration cancelled classes due to the riots. Everyone was restless and bored. He called Leah and asked if he could come over to visit. They lived less than half a mile from each other. He walked over. They made love one last time, a last hurrah post-breakup, acknowledging their continued feelings for each other, and stirred in part by the excitement and fear of the riots in the surrounding neighborhoods.[12] Yes, they had oral, vaginal, and anal sex. No, Leah wasn't "in" to anal sex, but she wanted to try it. She was experimenting with her sexuality, that's what young people do.

He never saw her again. He did not go to her house at all on Thursday, April 12.

The court took a recess after Damon's direct-examination testimony. Lehane started in with cross a half-hour later. Damon admitted he

---

[12] This phenomenon would repeat itself around the country with many people in the aftermath of 9/11.

was right-handed. He admitted to making love with Leah on her bed on multiple occasions over the years.

The general rule for lawyers when cross-examining a witness is to never ask a question you don't know the answer to, because the witness can sandbag you, or hurt you, or say something unexpected to undermine your case. In civil cases, this is easy to avoid, because you can depose the witness prior to trial and you know what he will say. But in criminal trials, the defendant rarely takes the stand, and given his Fifth Amendment right not to incriminate himself, the prosecutor can't depose the defendant. Lehane took a calculated risk on a set of questions involving Damon's prior sexual experience. Damon admitted he had sex with three other girls prior to Leah. Lehane would use that testimony at closing argument to undercut Damon's squeaky-clean, "I have sex for religious reasons" image. Lehane had nothing to lose; Damon would argue it anyway, so if he really had no other partners, Lehane lost little. But if Damon admitted to other partners, Lehane could score some points.

Lehane spent a lot of time grilling Damon about the breakup and the subsequent sexual encounter the day before Leah's death. Damon admitted that he agreed to the breakup on Saturday. He said it made sense given the different trajectories their lives were taking. Lehane kept at Damon about the breakup. This was a considered decision by Leah. Lehane got Damon to admit that Leah had talked with him before Saturday about the possibility of breaking up. Leah did not make a hasty decision; it was a well thought out consideration. Lehane got Damon to admit the fact that on Saturday he agreed to breakup with Leah, no recriminations, no anger. Yet out of the blue, when he calls her, Leah invites him over for one last "booty call" (objection, by Jones) on Wednesday. The sex on Wednesday with Leah was consensual? Yet, there was trauma to Leah's rectum and vagina. The other guy did that, Damon tried to rehabilitate himself. Damon said Leah had never had anal sex before that day. Had Damon in his prior sexual encounters? Yes, he admitted. Did he use lubrication when engaging in anal sex with a girlfriend? Yes, he did. What kind of lubricant? Something that Leah had around the house. Lehane must have been smiling inwardly when Damon said this because he had one last witness to call now for his rebuttal case.

Lehane wanted to know where Damon was on the afternoon of Thursday, April 12, the day Leah died. Damon testified that he went to see the riots. By himself. He had no alibi witnesses who could support that contention. He did not mention the motel tryst with the older woman.

The most damaging aspect of Lehane's cross-examination concerned Damon's statement to Simon Bergdorf on the day after Leah's death that Damon had not seen Leah since the Saturday before her murder. Yet, here Damon testified in court, under oath, that he did, in fact, see Leah again the day before she died. So, was Damon lying today, under oath? Or did he lie to Detective Bergdorf on Friday, April 13?

249

On re-direct, Jones tried to get Damon to testify that he was scared when the detectives showed up and started asking questions about Leah. He didn't tell the truth then because he didn't know what to say or how it might be misconstrued.

The defense rested its case after Damon's testimony. Matt Lehane had just one witness for his rebuttal case. He called the assistant coroner, Allison Pollard, back to the stand. He asked her if she found any kind of lubricant in Leah's rectum when she did the autopsy. "No," Pollard answered, sticking a dagger in the heart of Damon's defense.

Chapter Thirty-Nine

The Verdict

Judge Burger took another recess and then had the lawyers come back in the mid-afternoon for closing arguments. Lehane led off, as the prosecution holds the burden of proof.

Lehane admitted to me when I interviewed him for this book that he was very worried about this trial. Damon made a credible witness. No question he and Leah had sex within twenty-four hours before she died. But was that consensual sex the day before as Damon posited? Or was it rape and murder on the afternoon of April 12? With the high burden of proof a prosecutor must overcome, Lehane worried that the jury would hang, or maybe even vote for acquittal.

He walked the jury through the evidence. Prosecutors have two cracks at the jury during closing arguments. Because the prosecutor bears the burden of proof, he or she gets to go first, and after the defense attorney addresses the jury, the prosecutor gets one last chance on rebuttal to talk to the jury. Prosecutors leave the good stuff, the conclusions, not just the facts, for rebuttal.

Isaiah Jones spent a lot more time than Lehane. He reminded the jury of Damon's good character, asked the jury to consider his demeanor and his testimony. He reminded the jury of the high burden of proof the State must overcome to garner a conviction. "Except in this case, the State hadn't even come close. Damon had a reasonable explanation for his DNA in Leah's body." He pointed out that the DNA from the scrapings under Leah's nails did not match Damon's. Jones reminded the jury that the criminologists found a set of unknown fingerprints on the statue that someone used to bludgeon Leah with. "They weren't Damon's fingerprints. Is the State claiming that Damon acted out in rage and passion, and then took the time to dispassionately wipe his fingerprints from the bronze statue to cover up his crime? You can't have it both ways. It was either premeditated murder or a crime of passion.

"What about the mystery woman and the mystery man in her car? Maybe they did it. Or more likely, it was the creepy Vernon Banks, the guy who spied on Leah outside the window when she played piano, the man who sexually assaulted at least four teen girls. Four that we know about, because those four crimes are the ones he was charged with and went to prison for. Vernon did it, and the only reason the cops didn't find his DNA inside Leah is because, dumb as Vernon is, he was smart enough to wear a condom. And don't forget the sick porn the detectives found on his computer. Yes, torture porn. Just like what happened to poor Leah. Damon is very sorry for the Marcus family loss. For the loss of his girlfriend. But he's not the guy. He's just an innocent man caught up in a Franz

Kafka trial-like nightmare where the power of the State is brought down on the head of a man who can't escape its clutches."

Then Isaiah raised the race card. He reminded the jury that someone murdered Leah right in the middle of the riots. "The CPD garnered a lot of bad publicity stemming from the Tim Thomas shooting. Then this white girl gets murdered in a mixed neighborhood and, naturally, the cops zero in on her black boyfriend. Classic. A quick investigation that clears a murder shows the police department still can solve crimes. All neat, tied up with a pretty little ribbon. There's no evidence except for the DNA. Damon has a reasonable explanation for the DNA. So what do the police do? They double down on Damon. They don't really bother looking at the alternatives. Damon fits their narrative, and society's narrative, of the jealous ex-boyfriend killing the girl. Except this time, they get the added bonus of being able to add the angry black man to the narrative."

Of course, Lehane was objecting to all of this. None of this "information" was admitted as evidence at trial. Burger sustained the objections. But the damage was done. The jury heard what Isaiah had to say, and no instruction from the judge to ignore Jones's words could actually make the jury forget.

Lehane stood up to address the jury one last time. For his rebuttal, he reminded the jurors that, most compelling, the crime lab matched DNA from semen found in Leah's body to Damon. "A quadrillion to one." He repeated the odds. "Unmistakable. Damon had sex with

Leah. Do you, the jury, believe it was the day before? Or the day of Leah's murder, when an enraged and jealous ex-boyfriend took a final, humiliating revenge on his ex? Damon lied to you at trial. He either lied about not seeing Leah since Saturday or he lied to you under oath about having sex with Leah again, conveniently, in his case, the day *before* she died. In either event, he is a liar. How can you trust anything he says? He has no alibi for his whereabouts. His semen and fingerprints are all over the crime scene. He had a motive. My burden is to prove to you he committed the crime beyond a reasonable doubt—not beyond a shadow of a doubt. All this business about a mystery man in the car or Vernon Banks, it's all smoke and mirrors. He wants to deflect your vision from the evidence that ties him, the very evidence inside Leah's body, to her rape and death. That business about anal sex with lubricant? Just another lie. He didn't experiment gently with Leah and anal sex. He punished her without lubrication."

By this time, the clock read 4:45 so Burger adjourned court for hopefully the last time. He sequestered the jury for one more night. The trial would resume on Friday, August 24.

The next morning, Burger gave the jury its instructions as to the law of the case. This was an all or nothing case for Damon. Either he raped and murdered Leah or he didn't. There could be no lesser included offenses.

The jury retired to its deliberation room. The parties, lawyers, and families stayed in the courthouse. Criminal lawyers will tell you that if a jury returns a verdict soon, that often favors the prosecution. The longer they talk and deliberate, the more likely at least one juror is not in favor of voting for a conviction. Seventy-five minutes after the jury started its deliberations, it sent a note via the bailiff to the judge. They had reached a verdict.

Judge Burger called all the parties back to the courtroom and then had the jury file in. The jury foreperson handed the verdict form to the bailiff who handed it to the judge. The TV cameras rolled. People held their breath. Burger announced the verdicts.

Guilty on the charge of rape. Guilty on the charge of aggravated murder.

Damon hung his head in disbelief. A buzz erupted in the courtroom. The Marcus family and supporters glad for justice for their Leah. The Allbright family and supporters stunned that another travesty of justice against a black man had just taken place. Burger let the emotions boil over for a few moments, then banged his gavel to call order. He thanked the jury for their service and discharged them. He revoked Damon's bail and remanded his custody to the sheriff's office. Pre-sentence investigation by the Probation Department would proceed. Court would resume on September 7 for sentencing.

Chapter Forty

Reactions to the Verdict and Sentencing

In those moments after the court announced the verdicts, I had a difficult time observing everything that I needed to in order to write the story. I wanted Damon's reaction, but also those of his parents, the Marcuses, the lawyers, the jury, the judge, and the spectators. My head swiveled back and forth trying to gauge all these people's reactions.

Damon, as I said, hung his head. Isaiah clasped Damon's shoulder with his hand and gave a gentle squeeze and whispered something in his ear. The looks on Ben's and Sarah's faces combined relief and gratitude. A subtle upturning of the corners of Sarah's mouth, not quite a smile nor yet a smirk, suggested both victory and validation. I half expected Ben to look up and point to the sky, the way football players who score a touchdown do, thanking Jesus for the victory, until I remembered that Ben was Jewish.

Delores Allbright put her hand to her mouth but not before an audible sob escaped her lips. Othello's jaw tightened, and he squeezed his eyes almost to slits, either in an effort not to see what had just transpired or to hold in his rage that he feared would boil over. He told me that when I interviewed him in 2012. He knew yet another travesty of justice took place under his very nose, but making a scene in the courtroom would not help him or Damon's cause.

Lehane walked over to Jones and shook his hand, congratulating him on a hard-fought case. Judge Burger looked like he would have voted for conviction. The spectators who weren't related to the Allbrights or the Marcuses turned to one another and a louder hubbub flooded the courtroom as they discussed the verdict.

The jurors, none of whom looked Damon in the eye as they walked into the courtroom before the verdict announcement, left as quickly as the judge dismissed them. Lawyers will tell you that if the jury looks at the defendant when they walk in, they voted for acquittal; conversely, if they refuse to look at the defendant, the verdict favors the prosecution. Within a few days of the verdict, I managed to interview four of the jurors, including the two black jurors. I asked these people what made them vote to convict. The jurors, interviewed separately, told me the same story. They didn't believe Damon's story of consensual sex the day before Leah died. Lehane's impeachment of Damon with his inconsistent statement to the detectives weighed heavily in the jury's calculation. Then, as jurors are wont to do, they used common sense in their deliberations. They noted that Leah broke off the relationship. Damon allegedly acquiesced in her decision. Yet, a few days later, they were back to having sex again? They found that highly unlikely. They bought in to Lehane's version of a jealous ex-boyfriend.

The jury did not believe that Leah consented to anal sex, especially since Damon had testified that she never engaged in it previously. Why would she do so with a man she never intended to date again? When he testified that he used lubricant, but the coroner rebutted that testimony stating she found no lubricant inside Leah's body, that sealed Damon's fate. Inside the jury room, the six women jurors impressed upon their male colleagues that that was totally unbelievable. Few women like or are interested in anal sex, and since it can be painful, no woman would want to try it without lubricant. Certainly not a woman who was about to try if for the first time. Funny how the lack of a tube of KY jelly condemned Damon to an incarcerated future.

I attempted to interview the Marcuses and Damon's parents, but again, they rebuffed my efforts. So I charged off back to the *Tribune*'s offices to type up my story for the paper. All weekend long, the Allbright trial captivated the public. Not just the newspaper and TV reports, but the talk radio shows exploded with comments, for and against the verdict. After a while, I couldn't even listen to the vitriol spewed over the radio waves. Somewhere in all the finger-pointing, people lost sight of the fact that Leah Marcus was dead and the world was a lesser place because of that loss.

On Friday, September 7, Damon returned to Judge Burger's courtroom, in an orange jumpsuit this time. Burger had some discretion under the sentencing statutes. For a conviction of aggravated murder committed during a rape, he had a range of options. The penalty ranged from life in prison with no possibility of parole until after twenty, twenty-five, or thirty years up to life without possibility of parole. Burger reviewed the Probation Department's pre-sentence report. There is a funny dynamic when it comes to criminal defendants who roll the dice, go to trial, and lose. While they have a constitutional right to a jury trial, judges don't like jury trials. Jury trials take a lot of court time and make judges' dockets run more slowly. When the wheels of justice grind on, defendants whom juries convict get rolled over by those wheels. Judges, even ones not nicknamed "the Hammer," like Judge Burger, will often "throw the book" (within sentencing guidelines) at the convicted criminal. This is the dirty little secret of sentencing. Defense lawyers know this and advise their clients this might happen.

In light of all of the factors, including Damon's age and lack of a criminal record, Burger sentenced Damon to life with possibility of parole after twenty-five years. He sentenced Damon to a concurrent eleven-year sentence on the rape.[13] Damon would be forty-three years old before he would be eligible to take his case to a parole hearing.

All weekend long, the debate in Cincinnati about Damon's case continued. On Monday, September 10, Isaiah Jones filed a notice of

---

[13] The rape conviction carried a possible sentence of three to eleven years.

appeal. He also filed a motion to have the court appoint new counsel for Damon. The Allbrights could no longer afford to pay Isaiah's legal fees. Besides, the appeal would be premised in part upon an argument of ineffective assistance of counsel. Isaiah couldn't argue that claim himself. Because the appeal alleged no claims of constitutional issues, the final stop for Damon's case would be the Court of Appeals. He would either lose there, and serve out his sentence, or hope that the court would overturn the conviction. That result, while appreciated, would not solve Damon's problems. The State could always retry him.

The day before, in a country few Americans had heard of, no less could find on a map, the Taliban assassinated the resistance commander of the Northern Alliance, Ahmad Shah Massoud. They sent assassins posing as a television interviewer and his cameraman. The camera held a bomb which exploded during the interview, killing Massoud. This event was duly noted by the American media on the day that Damon filed his appeal; although, no one in the United States understood the exact implications of that act.

We all went to bed on September 10 expecting sunny skies and a beautiful fall-like day coming in the morning. That next day, I had a nasty sinus infection and went to my doctor's office. In the waiting room, the *Today* show aired on a TV monitor and I watched the aftermath of Mohamed Atta flying American Airlines Flight 11 into the North Tower of the World Trade Center at 8:46 a.m. Seventeen minutes later, United

Airlines Flight 175 crashed into the South Tower. While I might have ascribed the first incident as an accident, I, and everyone else, knew after the second plane hit that this was a terror attack.

The world that I understood mutated before my very eyes. Cincinnati had a new obsession to worry about, and it had nothing to do with Damon Allbright.

Chapter Forty-One

Post-Trial and Fast Forward

Also on Monday the tenth of September, my editor gave me a new assignment. I caught a plum one. I would write an in-depth series of articles on the Allbright trial. The research would start the next day. Except that the next day was September 11, 2001. Even now, I can recall my shock and horror at the events of that day. For people of my parents' and grandparents' generations, it must have been the same as the news of the Pearl Harbor attack. Numbness. Grief. Pain.

Except I was a reporter, and the newspaper didn't just let us sit around the watercooler and watch events transpire on TV. We had to make a plan of action. Get out there and start coverage. My editor pulled me off the Marcus/Allbright deep background report and assigned me, along with virtually every other reporter not related to sports or weather, to cover the 9/11 events. Unbeknownst to me at that time, or probably most Americans, I would have been surprised to find that coverage has never really stopped. In the aftermath of the terror attacks, we engaged in two wars in two different countries and our armed forces remain embedded in distant lands to this day.

I wrote countless articles for the *Tribune* about the war on terror from 2001 until the paper laid me off in 2011. Of course, I continued as the local crime reporter. Despite the notoriety of the Marcus case, crime did not cease after the riots and Leah's death. Murders continued in the greater Cincinnati area, and I continued to cover those events.

Damon did get a new attorney appointed by the court who handled the appeal. The court denied his motion to be released on bond pending appeal. The new lawyer, paid for by taxpayer dollars, filed a brief. Her argument focused on three elements relating to ineffective assistance of counsel. Isaiah Jones never should have put Damon on the stand. Conversely, Isaiah should have put forth Damon's alibi defense. Isaiah did not effectively challenge the DNA evidence.

The Court of Appeals heard oral arguments on the case on June 6, 2002. On August 14, the court published its opinion affirming the decision of the trial court. Damon's new lawyer filed a motion to ask the Ohio Supreme Court to review the case, but that court declined. Damon had no further appeals process; time had run out on his efforts to gain a new trial and perhaps an acquittal. Judge Burger committed Damon to the Warren Correctional Institution. That prison sits on a campus in Lebanon, Ohio, one county to the north of Hamilton County. This afforded Damon's family and friends an easy opportunity with a short drive to visit when they wanted. Later, when I did the interviews for this book, I drove a mere half hour to gain access to Damon.

With the Ohio Supreme Court decision declining review, the Allbright case concluded. Damon would be forty-three before he could petition the parole board to be let out of jail. He would be middle-aged by then. The year would be 2026. With the plethora of other crime cases, and of course, the whole post-9/11 saga, my reporter's eye fastened on other news items. The riots started to recede from the memory of Cincinnatians. Calm returned to the city. The police made improvements in procedure and hiring thanks to the Collaborative Agreement. Newspapers focus on news, which by implication, are those stories that are "new." The Marcus case, and the riots, they were old news, no longer worthy of reporting given all the changes in the world.

Racial tensions still flared throughout this country. Ferguson, Missouri; Baltimore, Maryland; Oakland, California; and many other communities suffered racial conflagrations. Sometimes Cincinnati made the news as a city that learned from its mistakes and implemented ways to bridge the racial divide.

Time passed. I continued reporting on the issues the *Tribune* decided were newsworthy. In the news business, 2011 turned out to be a pivotal year, and for me personally. Noteworthy stories from that year included the attempted assassination of Representative Gabby Giffords of Arizona, the Arab Spring, the killing of Osama bin Laden, Occupy Wall Street, and the repeal of

Don't Ask, Don't Tell. Yet, despite all these events, the *Tribune* struggled to stay afloat. Print newspapers get money from sales of newspapers, but mostly from advertising. With the advent of digital advertising, papers lost huge amounts of revenue. In addition, people sought out news from sources other than print newspapers, especially digital sources. Papers responded by rolling out digital issues, but the economics dictated that without advertising, papers would suffer. Some newspapers experimented with a subscription model. The *Wall Street Journal* navigated this transition. The *Tribune,* not so. People in Cincinnati just were not going to pay for a local paper as they might for a national one like the *Journal.* Plus, the *Enquirer* engaged in a duel with the *Tribune* for readers. With declining revenues, it was clear to the publisher that Cincinnatians simply would not support two local papers.

Two weeks after Seal Team Six killed Osama bin Laden, the *Tribune* notified its staff that it would shutter the presses in thirty days. (The joke around the *Tribune* watercooler was that the *Enquirer* News Team Six killed the *Tribune.*) I was heartbroken and devastated. My personal identity was wrapped up in my job. I was the crime reporter. Except, by June 13, I lost my job. I can't describe for you the lump in my throat when I applied to the hated *Enquirer* for a job. I don't know what was worse. Applying to work for the enemy, being turned down by them, or, had they hired me, having to work for them. In any event, they rejected my application and I filed for unemployment. I spent several months applying for other newspaper jobs in other cities. I didn't really want to leave my hometown, but I was the sole support of my family. I needed a job. As I accumulated rejection notice after notice (electronically, of course; by then, no one received an analog rejection letter), I had an epiphany. Print newspaper journalism, if not dead, was dying. I best look for another type of work.

I settled on freelance writing. I possessed skills useful for this occupation. I knew how to research and how to write. Plus, I didn't have to go back to trade school or college to retool into another profession. I didn't have the money to do that nor did I want to take out student loans. Not to mention it would have been hard to go to school full-time and still work, even back to waitressing or something, to pay the bills while I attended school.

Freelance gigging turned out to be liberating. The income came in on a sporadic basis, but the money was decent enough. A few hundred dollars here or there for an article a few hundred words long. Sometimes even more money. Believe it or not, my first article appeared in *Better Homes and Gardens*. But others followed, in a variety of magazines on a variety of topics from health, crime, of course (*Readers Digest*), fitness, and more. *Women's Health*, *Midwest Living*, *Self*, *Health*, and, I hate to admit it, *Cosmopolitan* ("Ten Secrets to Seducing a Man!") all followed.

With my newfound freedom came something else new—the almost unrestrained demand on my time. I could research and write my freelance articles whenever and wherever I wanted. Plus, these were short articles that didn't require loads of time. I didn't have to go to an office anymore or spend at least ten hours a day at a job, including commuting. There was only so much vacuuming and Swiffering I could do around the house. I found my attention coming back to the Leah Marcus case.

As a crime reporter, I have a tendency to look at criminal cases with a somewhat jaundiced eye. The cops and prosecutors get the right guy most of the time. But errors have occurred in the past. People would want to know. Did Damon get convicted of a crime he didn't commit? I found my thoughts going back to that case on a regular basis. What about Vernon Banks? A sex offender living three doors down the street with his fingerprints on the windowsill? The mystery woman in the car? Was she just a defense red herring, or did she have something to do with Leah's murder? The physical evidence also pointed to someone other than Damon. Why weren't his fingerprints found on the bronze statue if he really bashed her in the head with it? And whose DNA exactly was that under Leah's fingernails if not that of the killer? And if the killer was Damon, why didn't the fingernail DNA match his?

Over the summer of 2011, with my newfound freedom, I decided to do something I had never done before. I would write a book. And in the process, those still interested in the case might learn who really did kill Leah Marcus.

Chapter Forty-Two

First Steps, Ten Years After

True crime is its own genre, almost an art form now. I had no idea how to write a book about a real case. My writing efforts began with reading. I started with the book that revolutionized the genre, Truman Capote's *In Cold Blood*, about the murder of a Kansas family in their home in 1950 by two psychopaths looking for a treasure that didn't exist. Next, I read *Helter Skelter: The Shocking Story of the Manson Murders*, by Vincent Bugliosi, the prosecutor who handled the case. Erik Larson's *The Devil in the White City* juxtaposed the glory of the Chicago World's Fair, celebrating the four hundredth anniversary of Columbus arriving in the New World, with one of America's first serial killers, who stalked young women drawn to the fair. You should read Larson sometime; he writes non-fiction, but it reads like a novel. *Columbine* by Dave Cullen. The name says it all. In total, I read twenty-one books about true crime before I ever tried to organize writing one myself.

True crime fascinates the reading public for many reasons. People are fascinated by evil. These stories always involve death, a human inevitability. Many of them involve sex, a basic human need and desire. Readers of true crime wonder whether they, too, might be capable of committing such deeds. Does true crime allow the reader to air out his sadistic fantasies in a safe environment? Does it make our empathy and compassion grow for victims and possibly the murderers, who themselves were often victims of violence and abuse? Reading true crime is like watching a train wreck—you just can't look away. True crime triggers fear, one of the most basic and adrenaline-surging emotions that humans experience. Reading about real-life murders is a guilty pleasure for thrill-seeking adults. We can stand over the abyss, no, hang over it, from the safety of a harness and never actually fall in, yet still get a good look. That's why people read it. We want to deny that our prim and proper selves are burdened by lust, greed, anger, and revenge, when, of course, all of us have those emotions. We just usually keep them under better wraps than the people we read about, who go about committing true crimes.

Before I interviewed my first subject, I got my hands on everything ever written about the case. I read news articles on the riots and Leah's murder. I read the stories in national magazines and people's blogs. Various media ran reports on the murder and the trial. I gained access to television videos and listened to or read the transcripts of radio programs such as NPR that covered the murder and trial. I read the entire transcript of Damon's trial. A friend of mine got me access to Allison Pollard's autopsy report and the autopsy photographs. (This friend probably committed a crime, so I won't print her name here.)

I recorded all my in-person interviews. Fortunately, the key players I chose to interview still lived in the greater Cincinnati area. All except Alice Bowman, who passed away at age eighty-eight in 2009. Proximity allowed me the luxury of interviewing these people in person, whereas telephone calls or email exchanges would have prevented me from assessing their body language when I questioned them. I had no particular order of people I wanted to interview, other than I wanted to leave Ben and Sarah Marcus to the last, perhaps to give them hope that I was getting close to finding out the truth behind their daughter's death.

Getting people to agree to interviews when they knew I was going to write a book about their responses requires a certain degree of tact and coaxing. Many people were eager to help, such as Leah's friends. Others were more circumspect for legal reasons, such as Isaiah Jones who felt constrained by attorney-client privilege. Others had to be "threatened" in the sense that if they did not cooperate, I would still write about them based upon what I gleaned from other interviews and parts of the written record that I could analyze. Failure to cooperate meant that person would have little control over what I would put down in words. Vernon Banks was one of these people. Intimidation worked. After waffling on the issue, he agreed to let me interview him in 2015.

I turned my little used dining room into the Marcus/Allbright investigation headquarters.

I put corkboards on the wall and brought in whiteboards. I tacked three-by-five-inch index cards to the corkboards, affixed Post-it notes to the walls, and drew on, erased, and wrote over again on the whiteboards. No visitor dared venture into the dining room on pain of a severe penalty. I put the rule in place for two reasons. One, I didn't want anyone messing up my research or thoughts. Two, I didn't want anyone looking at my work or offering opinions about it.

While I doubted that Damon committed the crime, I did not exclude him. I had four whiteboards offering four different versions of the crime. Damon did it. Vernon Banks did it. The blonde lady ("Lady XX") with her shadowy accomplice in the car did it. Damon's defense theory that someone else killed Leah might be true, but the people he pointed the finger at, Vernon and the blonde, might be off target. The last board left open the option of a mystery killer that no one else knew about, "Mr. XY." (I hope you appreciate the puns of these last two unnamed killers based on male and female X and Y chromosomes.)

Chapter Forty-Three

Theory One: Damon Did It

One thing I knew as a long-time crime reporter and a budding *aficionada* of true crime: the cops and prosecutors usually get it right. As a consequence of that rule, an unintended corollary follows. On those occasions when they get it wrong, cops and prosecutors don't want to admit it. They will swear up and down they had the right man, but the judge or the jury or the high bar of the criminal burden of proof let a guilty man go free. These people need to be reminded of the quotation of William Blackstone, one of England's finest jurists, who wrote that, "Better that ten guilty persons escape than one innocent one suffer."[14] When journalists revisit sensational cases years after the verdicts, the detectives and prosecutors still want to argue they had the right man. This, I suspect, is human nature. They don't want to admit they were wrong. They don't want to think that all the effort they expended on an investigation or a trial convicted an innocent man. Nor do they want to think of the consequence to that poor

---

[14] Blackstone's *Commentaries on the Law of England*, circa 1760.

innocent man who spent years locked up in prison for a crime he didn't commit. Sometimes, police and lawyers are protecting themselves, or their colleagues, or their department. Rarely do you find one who will concede the *possibility* that they got it wrong.

I am pleased to report to you that neither Simon Bergdorf nor Matt Lehane fell into that trap. Both men struck me as willing to consider the evidence. I interviewed Bergdorf in 2011 and Lehane in 2012. Both men still worked for their respective departments at the time I interviewed them. They both acknowledged the troubling aspects of the case. Many of those concerns I have already documented herein for the reader. Let me revisit in brief some of their concerns. Bergdorf found Damon's expression of shock and revulsion at the news of Leah's death as something one could not fake. Unless, he noted, one was a sociopath. Yet, nothing in Damon's background suggested sociopathic tendencies. Bergdorf's and Lehane's major consideration revolved around the DNA evidence found in Leah's body that matched Damon's. For many people, including professionals, DNA is the end all of criminal liability. It is, if you will, the silver bullet to kill the werewolf of crime. If the DNA fit, you must convict, to riff off a phrase Johnny Cochrane used to great effect in the O. J. Simpson trial regarding a certain bloodstained glove.

However, DNA evidence is much more complicated than detectives and prosecutors want to admit and may not be as reliable as previously thought.[15] Despite the early years' travails regarding the reliability of DNA collection and analysis, many criminal cases are now resolved with DNA. In fact, cases with DNA evidence tend to result in more convictions and juries expect to see such evidence. Standards in processing DNA evidence have improved. Even Barry Scheck, one of Simpson's lawyers, went on to head The Innocence Project that resulted in the overturning of hundreds of cases of people improperly convicted using DNA evidence.

Getting into the vagaries of DNA evidence is beyond the scope of this book. To spin a general tale, consider these facts. In the old days, criminalists needed a substantial amount of genetic material to make an analysis. Now, a drop of spittle is sufficient. Complicating DNA analysis is whether multiple persons' DNA is found in/on a victim. You and I share 99.9 percent of our DNA in common. However, somewhere along the double helix strands of

---

[15] The concept that once tried and true methods of crime lab methods and results have been either deflated or debunked is well known. Bite-mark analysis, a sort of dental fingerprinting used all the way back to the time of the Salem witch trials, has been debunked. The "uniqueness and reproducibility" of ballistics testing has been called into question by the National Research Council. The FBI recently admitted that it found errors in ninety percent of hair analysis cases. Of course, O. J.'s lawyers used contamination of DNA both at the scene of the crime and at the crime lab as a means to create doubt for the jury.

DNA in each of our cells is a repeatable pattern unique to me and not to you. Each of these variations, called an allele, needs to be compared in DNA analyses, and the standard nowadays is to use thirteen different alleles at different locations. A great description I read about DNA analysis is that there are many thousands of paintings with a green background, but fewer with a green background and blue flowers, and even fewer with a green background, blue flowers, and a yellow horse. Keep this up for at least thirteen comparisons, and you have your man. Or woman. To compare suspect A with suspect B, DNA requires a usual comparison of thirteen genetic markers, and if these match, the odds are at least a billion to one that you have the right person. But tiny specimen samples make it difficult to match at least thirteen alleles.

With mixtures of genetic material, the match gets even more complex. In Leah's case, there was her DNA and Damon's. Possibly more. Two people doubles the alleles that have to be matched, three people triples, and so on.

Trace amounts of DNA can lead to bizarre and unintended results. There was a case in California where a homeless man was implicated in the death of a millionaire because the suspect's DNA was found under the fingernail of the deceased man. The suspect had very minor criminal charges on his record. An EMT squad aided the homeless man for a medical emergency. The EMTs put a pulse-oxygen sensor on his finger and then used the same sensor on the decedent thereby transferring an innocent man's DNA to the dead man. In fact, the homeless man had been in a detox center at the time of the millionaire's death.

Damon's defense never argued that the DNA analysis was not accurate. He argued that, "Sure, we had sex. The day before Leah was murdered. Of course, my DNA was still in her body." The jury just didn't buy into Damon's credibility. But the jury never heard about Damon's alibi defense. Might that have made a difference?

When I initially interviewed Bergdorf and Lehane in 2011, I had not yet spoken to Damon or his lawyer and so I didn't know about Damon's alibi. (Those interviews took place in 2013 and 2015 for Damon and 2014 for Isaiah Jones.) I went back and interviewed the detective and the prosecutor a second time each in 2017 and posed them the question. If you knew Damon had an alibi, would that have made a difference? Both men waffled on the question. They would have wanted an opportunity to investigate the alibi, talk to Jones about his theory of the case. Based on the information I had available, they both said the alibi evidence was very weak and that was something that Damon would have the burden of proof upon, albeit a weaker preponderance of the evidence burden. Without a way to identify the mystery "freelance reporter," with no video from The Mallard's security cameras, neither man was really persuaded that Damon had a viable alibi. Which brought both men back to the credibility of Damon's story that he had sex with Leah the day before she died.

I know that somewhere along the line, Damon lied. He told Bergdorf the day after Leah's death that he hadn't seen his ex-girlfriend since their date six days before. Yet, at trial, he testified he not only saw her, but had sex with her, the day before she died. He testified that they had oral, vaginal, and anal sex. We know how Lehane grilled Damon over those two irreconcilable stories. One version of the truth might be Damon had sex with Leah either the day of or the day before Leah died. If they had sex the day of, then Damon is the killer. If the day before, then someone else killed, maybe or maybe not raping, her. If they raped her, they used a condom. Hence, no other suspect's DNA was found in Leah's body. *But no one ever checked to see if another person's DNA was commingled in with Damon's semen.* Damon lost his appeal, but with hindsight, we can look back and say that Jones should have filed a motion to have the DNA evidence re-examined by an independent expert to see if there was any other DNA involved. Perhaps Jones took Damon at his word, that he and Leah had sex the day before and that was the end of the matter.

Damon is, as I have reported, a highly intelligent man. He knew, so he says, based on a "hint" from Isaiah Jones, that he had to testify that he had sex with Leah the day before. If the jury believed his testimony, the result would be an acquittal. When I asked Damon at the Warren Correctional Institution if he wanted me to contact the University of Cincinnati College of Law Innocence Program, he declined. Why? The sign of a guilty man? Or was Damon hiding something else?

When I interviewed him, Damon said he hadn't seen Leah since the Saturday of their last date, but then quickly corrected himself to say the day before Leah's death. Why did he slip up? The truth seemed to be that he really hadn't seen Leah since April 7. And why did he testify that they had anal sex when he admitted they had never done so previously? What would spur Leah to try something so unusual during their last sexual encounter after they had already broken up? Why did he lie to Isaiah Jones that he, Damon, had anal sex with her when he implied to me that he had not? Did he not disclose his alibi to his parents only because he was embarrassed about his encounter with "the reporter" and the shame it would bring upon him? Was his shame and mortification sufficient to outweigh the risk that he might go to prison for a long time by not putting forth his alibi?

What if Damon really never had sex with Leah after Saturday? Would his DNA still be in her body five days later? Could Isaiah Jones have found an expert who would have posited that? In a battle of experts, that might have been enough doubt created in the minds of the jurors to acquit Damon. I have found research that suggests that sperm cells can still be found in a woman's reproductive tract up to seven days after coitus, which fits with this timeline of Damon's innocence.

If Damon killed Leah in a jealous boyfriend rage as Lehane posited, then two pieces of evidence don't fit the supposition. Why weren't Damon's fingerprints found on the bronze statue the assailant clubbed Leah with? Why wasn't his DNA found under her fingernails?

If we assume that Damon acted in a jealous rage, we rule out any effort of premeditation ("prior calculation and design" to use the language of the statute) that Damon planned all along to kill Leah. If he planned to kill, wiping his prints off the statue makes sense. He also would have used a condom so as not to leave DNA evidence in her body. But if he killed her in a jealous rage, then he would not have made any efforts to cover his tracks. Lehane can't argue it both ways. Either it was premeditated or a jealous rage, but Damon couldn't have committed both crimes at the same time.

Also, if Leah fought back in the minutes before her death, she scratched her assailant with her hands. Yet, Damon's DNA was not found under her nails. So whose DNA was that?

At the least, it seems to me, there was enough evidence to demonstrate sufficient doubt that the State had not met its high burden of proof. At best, one can argue that Damon was convicted of a crime he did not commit.

But if Damon didn't kill Leah, who did?

Chapter Forty-Four

Theory Two: Vernon Banks Did It

"I never really liked Vernon Banks for the murder," Simon Bergdorf told me. "He didn't fit the profile. Yes, he was a pedophile. And, yes, we had his fingerprints at the Marcus house. But he was a sex offender who molested, okay raped, adolescent girls without an actual physical beating. He wasn't into violence. Beyond the sexual violence, obviously." Or so the detectives thought at the beginning of the investigation. I reminded Simon of the torture porn they found on Banks's computer. "He liked to daydream of what it would be like. I pulled his old files, talked to the detectives involved in those cases. He never tortured his victims. He never tied them up. He threatened force, but never used it." I inquired whether Vernon's appetites had changed over time. Whether being in prison and the subject himself of physical abuse might have caused a spark to ignite darker fantasies in his mind. Bergdorf admitted the possibility but doubted that really happened.

When I met with Vernon Banks in 2015, I wanted to meet on neutral ground. I didn't want to be alone in his house, and I certainly did not want him knowing where I lived. We met at a well-used dog park, full of people to whom I could call for help if Vernon had any intention of causing me physical harm, but far enough away from us that we could talk and no one would overhear our conversation. It was a beautiful spring day, with the smell of flowers in bloom, the sound of barking dogs, and the occasional growl of an animal asserting dominance or telling another to back off.

Vernon reiterated to me the same narration he told Bergdorf. Vernon had seen Leah in the neighborhood, knew who she was, but had nothing to do with her demise. He was cured. "Or at least in remission," he told me when I reminded him of all the porn the detectives found on his computer. Banks didn't want to go back to prison; that had been traumatic enough. He knew if he committed another infraction he would probably get a life sentence. It was safer to watch porn than to accost any more girls.

When I spoke with Bergdorf four years prior to my interview with Banks, Simon filled me in on a lot of what Banks had been up to. I knew that Banks preyed on petite, brunette girls. Leah fit that description. She lived three houses down the street. Seeing her, I asked him, that must have been so tempting. He had heard her playing the piano many times, he admitted. Such a pretty, talented girl. That must have excited him. There is your dream victim right down the street. He denied it. Yet, I posed the question, you didn't exactly ignore her either. He walked up and down that street on many occasions, had heard her playing the piano, had seen her

281

walking in the neighborhood. He knew I knew about his fingerprints on Leah's windowsill. Okay, he admitted; "so I peeped on her once. But just because of the music she was playing. Her piano playing was so beautiful." Drawing a distinction between his attraction to her musical skills versus her physical self that happened to coincide with the type of girl he assaulted in the past is a fine line, I pointed out. He swore he had never been in her house and had only peered in the window that one time. When was that one time, I asked? "About four weeks before the riots," he said, "when it was still dark out at night and no one would see me spying." The timing alone is suspicious, wouldn't you agree, I asked him.

Vernon projects a persona of a somewhat bumbling, uneducated, downtrodden, meek individual. Yet, something inside him allows a more dominating, physically intimidating character to peek out at times, certainly when he abused the four girls whose cases caused Banks's legal problems. There were probably more than just those four, I asked him. He denied it, of course. We know that sexual predators continue their predations and rarely stop, unless something significant happens, such as their death, their incarceration, or something so unusual, an escapade gone wrong, where they almost got caught. Like people with OCD, they have an obsession and a compulsion to keep acting unless and until they can't anymore.

Who can say what turns a convicted pedophile into a more dangerous rapist and murderer? The evidence was tantalizing. We know Vernon Banks spent a lot of time at home watching sick things on his computer, fantasizing; what would it be like to really do that? We know that Vernon lived three doors down the street from a petite, beautiful teenager, just the sort of person who would ignite his fetishes and fantasy world. We know that Vernon Banks spied on Leah through the window of her piano room.

No one in the neighborhood, other than Vernon's parents, knew that he was a sex offender. Leah would not have been on the alert about him. Sarah and Ben never knew about Vernon's proclivities until after the murder, and even then, they didn't know about Banks's identity as the predator until I told them about him when I interviewed them in 2016 and 2017. Before I mentioned Banks as a sex offender, Sarah, who I assume knew more about Leah's life than Ben simply because Sarah was the mother and spent more time with Leah, never said that Leah was concerned or worried about Banks.

Leah presented an opportunity and a challenge for Vernon. Here he was, a powerless man robbed of his station and due in life, forced to live in his parents' attic. Yet, down the street lived this rich, beautiful, talented girl, the epitome of a sexual partner that he could never hope to obtain in the usual method of courtship. To obtain power over such a target must have tempted Vernon to his core.

It is not a huge leap of faith to suspect that Banks's fantasies morphed over time from not only abusing girls but to hurting them. To act out on those fantasies, using Leah as his victim, we can assume that Vernon would use careful planning in his preparations. Attacking a random victim is one thing; assaulting a girl who lives three houses down the street is another thing. Leah would be able to identify Vernon if she survived an assault. If Vernon's intention was to sexually assault and torture Leah, then somewhere in his calculations he must have known he would have to kill her to prevent her from identifying him as her assailant.

Since Leah knew Banks as a neighbor, it is reasonable to believe that she would have opened the door to him on the day she died. Once he gained access, it was a few short feet to the credenza in the foyer to pick up the bronze statute and bludgeon Leah with it. But, you ask, what about his fingerprints? The police didn't find Vernon's prints on the statue, just some random, unknown person's. The simple answer is that Vernon slipped on gloves before he bashed in Leah's head. Keeping gloves on during the rest of the time he spent in the house, the police never found any prints inside the house. Vernon simply forgot that one time in the past when he peered through the piano room window that he touched the sill and left his prints there. When he raped Leah, he wore a condom so he didn't leave any DNA. For all we know, Vernon shaved his body hair so that no Caucasian body or pubic hair was found in Leah's bedroom. Fortunately and unbeknownst to Vernon, the police found Damon's DNA inside Leah's body, and, like a heat-seeking missile, they flew off after that jealous ex-boyfriend.

But that troubling DNA under Leah's nails presents a problem in concluding that Vernon was the killer. His DNA did not match that which Leah scraped off of her attacker. The crime lab tested the scrapings under her nails, and they didn't match Vernon's buccal swab.

Chapter Forty-Five

Theories Three and Four: Suspects XX

and XY

If one operates under the assumption that neither Damon Allbright nor Vernon Banks killed Leah, then one should look at alternate theories, one thrown out at trial by Isaiah Jones that the blonde woman in the car, with perhaps a male companion, had something to do with Leah's demise. Or, perhaps, one could consider a whole other suspect, XY, a completely unknown subject.

Alice Bowman told detectives Bergdorf and Nowakowski, and also testified at trial, about the blonde woman. She came roaring into the neighborhood, yet went walking back deliberately towards the Marcus residence. Bowman implied that if you didn't already know where Leah lived, why would you come zooming into the neighborhood at way over the speed limit. And if you knew where she lived, why would you park four houses down the street and then walk back? The inference one can make from this is that XX didn't want her car anywhere near the Marcus house because of some nefarious deed she had planned. Bowman didn't see anyone in the woman's car, and the woman walked alone back towards the Marcus house. Given that Alice's house was slightly around the curve of the arc of the street, she couldn't directly see the Marcus home. So, one might infer that XX had already dropped a male companion off, at, or near Leah's house and was just parking the getaway car a fair distance away so as not to arouse anyone's suspicion that something criminal was about to happen at Leah's residence.

Bergdorf and Nowakowski found all the available closed-circuit TV film and home security camera views of XX's car. The grainy images never allowed identification of the car or a license plate. Bergdorf told me that one might be able to say that there was a companion in the passenger seat. Or, just as plausibly, one might say it was just a shadow. Whether it was a person, a male, or a mannequin, who could actually tell?

The blonde woman, with or without a male companion, actually fits the facts of the case. If a lone woman knocked on Leah's door, Leah might have let her in. A white woman would not appear threatening to Leah even amid the heightened tensions of the riot. After she clubbed Leah with the statue, Leah would have been incapacitated. This would have allowed time for XX's male companion to show up at the doorstep, let himself in, and help carry Leah up the stairwell to her bedroom. There, the male sexually assaulted Leah and wore a condom, leaving no telltale semen in Leah's body. Then again, since no one ran an independent analysis of the DNA evidence, maybe this male didn't wear a condom and his DNA might have been discovered, if only someone would run the tests. The DNA under the fingernails belongs either to XX or her companion. DNA, found in the nucleus of cells, is divided into twenty-three pairs of chromosomes, one of which came from a person's mother and one from her father. One pair of chromosomes determine sex characteristics of a person, the "X" and "Y" chromosomes. Nowhere in the record of Leah's case is there a determination regarding the sex of the person whose DNA was lifted from beneath Leah's fingernails. Yet, the evidence is still locked in the CPD evidence room, and it would be easy to determine if the person Leah scratched was a man or a woman.

How or why the blonde woman and her companion chose Leah remains a mystery. Had they targeted Leah? Was Leah a victim of opportunity? We may never know.

Then again, perhaps XX is nothing more than a red herring manufactured by Isaiah Jones. Maybe XY is the actual killer. This unknown male, again, whose motives remain unclear, fits the facts. You might think of him as some phantom menace straight out of a Cormac McCarthy novel. Perhaps he posed as a delivery driver or some other innocuous personage to whom Leah would open the door without trepidation. The unknown fingerprints on the statue and the unknown DNA under Leah's fingernails fits with an unidentified male subject. If he wore a condom, then none of his semen commingled with Damon's. Or, perhaps, he didn't wear one, but since no one ran an independent test, we don't know if more than one man deposited semen inside Leah.

When I spoke with Sarah Marcus in 2016, and then Ben Marcus in 2017, I ran all these theories and considerations through with both of them, independently. They had made up their minds that Damon was the killer and that justice had been served. I had my own theory as to which of these hypotheses fully explained Leah's death.

But, as with so many mysteries in life, the answer was more complex. Still waters run deep they say, and that was the case with Leah Marcus.

Chapter Forty-Six

Cold Dish[16]

I still see her face. After all these years. Hear the sound of her voice, the peal of her laugh. Smell the strawberry in the shampoo she used to wash her hair.

I wonder if the Marcuses dream all these thoughts about Leah. Ben Marcus, in particular, though Sarah was his enabler and abettor.

I fear that if I forgive him, my memory of her will fade, will abate so that even the sharpest memory will be a surreal, sepia print of a life that was but wasn't. Like a candle snuffed out, the only reminder of its light the wisp of smoke, and when that is gone, the smell of burnt wax and then nothing. I won't do that to her. It's why I

---

[16] The idea's origin is obscure. The French diplomat Charles Maurice de Talleyrand-Pérogord (1754–1838) has been credited with the saying, "La vengeance est un met que l'on doit manger froid." "Revenge is a dish that must be eaten cold." The expression suggests that revenge satisfies more if enacted when unexpected and/or long anticipated. It runs counter to traditional civilized revulsion to "cold-blooded" violence.

won't forgive him. She lives on in my hate. Every day, I resurrect her memory with my first breath, and she's there in my vision even as my eyes close and I am carried off to sleep by the soporific of temazepam—thanks to the kindness of my doctor.

I started smoking after she died. I don't know why, really. To calm me down, perhaps. To give me the fortitude to soldier on. Considering that I've only smoked for twenty-five years, I feel that death before sixty from "the Cancer," as my family called it, lung cancer in my case, seems ineluctably unfair. But, then again, perhaps not.

Back in the day, I was the Crime Reporter. That work gave my life meaning. I, a lexicological Charon, shepherded the souls of the victims through the criminal justice system and would report to their survivors the last words and breaths of those who killed their loved ones as the murderers lay strapped to the gurney in the death chamber at Lucasville State Prison.

Long before the scribes who wrote the Bible down, long before Greece and Rome ruled the world, a king in Mesopotamia proclaimed, "an eye for an eye, and a tooth for a tooth." Hammurabi's Code always made sense to me. A simple way to evaluate penalties for crimes. Everyone knows what will happen to them if they commit a certain crime. We've gotten away from that. Now we have mitigating and aggravating circumstances. The upbringing of the poor accused and his rights are taken into account when sentenced. What rights did he allow his victim? When he killed her?

My oncologist says I have only months to live. Therefore, I've typed this manuscript, while I still have the energy and the wherewithal. I will put it in my safe deposit box, and after my death, my lawyer will be instructed to send a copy to the Marcuses so they will know the truth of their daughter's senseless killing.

Her name was Jenny. She was ten. In 1995, she was ten years old and she called me at work that April day. Yes, April, as in the month Leah died. Jenny was at home, after school. A neighbor down the street watched her for me after she got off the bus and before I got home from work. Jenny wanted to ride her bicycle in the street, alone, no supervision. Mrs. Wilson, the sitter, made her call me at the office. Jenny had never ridden alone, unsupervised, in the street before. Mrs. Wilson knew that. But I was proud of my girl, how smart and grown up she was getting. How she knew enough to call to ask permission rather than surreptitiously break a cardinal rule. How unlike the modern sensibilities where people decide it's better to beg for forgiveness later than ask for dispensation ahead of time. I relented. It was a beautiful spring day. There was little traffic in the street yet. People were still at work.

I told Jenny it would be okay. I had her give the phone back to Mrs. Wilson and told her I gave her my indulgence. Mrs. Wilson said she would keep an eye on Jenny anyway.

I told her it would be okay.

Jenny strapped on her helmet, rolled her bike out of the garage, and happily rode up and down the street. Never so far, Mrs. Wilson told me later, that she couldn't see her. Fifteen minutes later, she pedaled up on the sidewalk in front of our house to ask Mrs. Wilson would she be able to make a pitcher of lemonade; it was such hot work riding her bicycle. Mrs. Wilson assured her that would be fine. Jenny waved her final goodbye, pointed her bike back towards the street, emerged into it between two parked cars.

Mrs. Wilson saw the car coming. Like most of us would have, she assumed the driver of the car saw Jenny and would slow down before it would be too late. She said she thought it was going fast. The driver of the car, a Mercedes, he never mashed the brakes. The Mercedes slammed into Jenny broadside just as she entered the street, she not being able to see around the parked vehicles.

Mrs. Wilson watched in horror as Jenny flew forty feet through the air. Mrs. Wilson told me she saw the driver, from her higher perspective up the slight hill from curbside, as she sat on my porch. He never slowed down, she said. He was talking on his cell phone. Distracted driving.

He stopped, at least. Got out of his car and ran to my child, who lay broken and bleeding in the street. Mrs. Wilson did, too. But there was nothing they could do. She was conscious, when Mrs. Wilson arrived, in pain, struggling to stay alive. She said, "Tell Mom..." Mrs. Wilson said she never finished the sentence and then died in her arms. The Mercedes man called the police. With his cell phone.

He was never convicted of a crime. Even though he was speeding and driving distracted by talking on his phone. The police charged him with several crimes, but the prosecutor couldn't make it stick. Before it came to trial, Mrs. Wilson recanted her testimony. Mercedes man had gotten to her, had paid her under the table to change her story. With the star witness non-cooperative, the case got dismissed. The license plate on the car read "CR 23."

I never heard of Ben Marcus before he ran my daughter down. Ran her down like a dog in the street, without thinking, without caring, without paying attention, and without a penalty. Doing what he could do, pulling levers, so that there would be no repercussions, except perhaps in the back of his mind, the deep well of the deep pocket of his soul.

I have a Shakespearian view of revenge. Waiting, biding my time, feeding my pain for years, stirring the slow boil of hatred. I never let your memory die, Jenny. Your body grew cold, as did my heart, frozen in a Siberian tundra for these last twenty-five years, but your memory, my love, your memory glows softly still in the recesses of my mind.

When the riots came along, I found my chance. Damon, forgive me, you were meant to be a pawn, true, but not one sacrificed in the game. There should have been enough doubt created in the case to get you off. Like the woman with the blonde hair. She was me, of course. A dye job, but me. Like the fingerprints on the bronze statue. They were mine. Like the DNA under Leah's fingernails. Mine, from where she scratched my face. After Leah's death, I cut my hair short and wore my glasses instead of my usual contact lenses. Damon never recognized me even though I sat one row behind him throughout the trial proceedings.

I did park down the street from Nine Burton Woods Lane. I did walk back to Leah's house, knocked on the door, and gave her a story about my car running out of gas, being worried about the riots. She let me in to borrow a phone. A fatal mistake.

I did spend the day with Damon at The Mallard Motel. I rented the room the previous day. There were no security cameras. Cash was king at The Mallard. No record of my being there, but if there was, it was under an assumed name. I fucked Leah's boyfriend, and he was an impressive exemplar of the male sex in bed. He wasn't a skilled lover, but what he lacked in adroitness, he more than made up for with vitality and eagerness. I harvested three condoms full of his semen, which I carefully collected without spilling a drop and later implanted in Leah's lifeless body.

When Nickelback released its hit that summer, I listened to it hundreds of times. For, oh, how Leah reminded me of my Jenny.

So, Ben Marcus, I stole from you that which you took from me. The books are closed now, the accounts reconciled. Karma exists, and it will reach out and touch you long after you think you got away with something. The universe is making its peace with me now. It gave me the Cancer. So there. The cold case murder mystery of Leah Marcus is no longer a mystery, just a tragedy for all involved.

My name you ask? Just call me the Crime. Reporter.

Notes on the Narrative

This book tells the story of a fictional murder set during the time of real events. As such, certain individuals, both living and deceased, are referenced in the narrative. No malice or harm was intended by me with regard to these persons. Invoking their presence was intended to increase the "reality" of the story and to blend with the journalistic/non-fiction tone of the book.

The following "characters" referenced in the story are real people. Where I ascribed statements to certain of these characters, as denoted by quotation marks around those comments, I have a primary source for each of these quotes as listed below.

Timothy Thomas (deceased), Angela Leisure,[17] Tywon Thomas,[18] Monique Crutchfield f.k.a. Wilcox, Stephen Roach, Roger Owensby Jr. (deceased), Al Gerhardstein, Carl Lindner (deceased), Henry James,[19] Harvey Price, Mike Allen, Ken Lawson, Deion Sanders, John Cranley, Alicia Reese, John Shirey, Tom Streicher, Jim

---

[17] Cincinnati Enquirer, 4/10/2001, NBC News, Dateline, http://www.nbcnews.com/id/4703574/ns/dateline_nbc-dateline_specials/t/behind-death-timothy-thomas/#.W-TepS-ZNns
[18] Cincinnati Enquirer, 12/22/2016, Section 1A
[19] World Socialist Website, https://www.wsws.org/en/articles/2001/05/cin1-m24.html

Tarbell, Roslyn Jones, Charlie Luken, Cristina Clark[20] Khaled Daqeer, Shawn Wiegand, Samuel Dubose (deceased), O. J. Simpson, Johnny Cochrane (deceased), and Barry Scheck.

In addition, the *Cincinnati Enquirer* is a real newspaper; the *Cincinnati Tribune* is a fictional one. There was a second daily newspaper in Cincinnati, the *Post,* that existed at the time of Leah's fictional death; it ceased doing business in 2007.

---

[20] Cincinnati Enquirer, 4/12/2001, Section A, p. 14

Acknowledgments

Writing a novel is not a solitary endeavor. Many people helped me along the way to get *And the River Runs Deep: The Cold Case Murder Mystery of Leah Marcus* into print. First and foremost, I especially thank Mark Piepmeier, Esq., Head of the Criminal Division of the Hamilton County, Ohio, Prosecutor's office, for steadfast encouragement and tutelage about the nuts and bolts of police investigation, court procedures, and trial tactics. Mark spent many hours reading the manuscript and talking with me via email and in person about this novel. Any errors in the manuscript concerning police or court procedures he pointed out to me. Those that remain I left because I thought they contributed to the narrative, the tension, and the drama of the story.

Thanks, also, to Robert Kidd and Courtney Galloway for their cogent editing work of the material. Your insights and suggestions that I incorporated into the final version of this work make it that much more readable.

Thanks also to my graphic artist extraordinaire, Dave Flege, who has now collaborated with me on three books covers. As always, you end up with an irreducible image for a book cover. Thanks as well to Shelley Savoy at Booknook for her work on the cover.

Also, Margie Ullman deserves a large shout-out for allowing me time and space to work countless days, nights, and weekends on this project. Thank you for your indulgence.

Barb Gerla was the earliest reader of the manuscript, and I appreciate her generous contribution of time and critique.

Made in the USA
Monee, IL
27 July 2020